Lyrics&
Over 60 Essential Songs
Chords

Published by
WISE PUBLICATIONS
14-15 Berners Street, London W1T 3LJ, UK.

Exclusive Distributors:
MUSIC SALES LIMITED
Distribution Centre, Newmarket Road,
Bury St Edmunds, Suffolk IP33 3YB, UK.
MUSIC SALES PTY LIMITED
Music Sales Pty Limited
20 Resolution Drive, Caringbah, NSW 2229, Australia.

Order No. AM999097
ISBN 978-1-84938-325-7
This book © Copyright 2009 Wise Publications,
a division of Music Sales Limited.

Music arranged by Matt Cowe
Music edited by Adrian Hopkins
Compiled by Nick Crispin
Music processed by Paul Ewers Music Design

Cover designed by Fresh Lemon
Cover photo and page 21 & 65 courtesy of Jacqui Black
All other photos courtesy of LFI

Printed in the EU

Your Guarantee of Quality
As publishers, we strive to produce every book to the
highest commercial standards. This book has been carefully
designed to minimise awkward page turns and to make
playing from it a real pleasure. Particular care has been
given to specifying acid-free, neutral-sized paper made from pulps
which have not been elemental chlorine bleached. This pulp is from
farmed sustainable forests and was produced with special regard
for the environment. Throughout, the printing and binding have
been planned to ensure a sturdy, attractive publication which
should give years of enjoyment. If your copy fails to meet our high
standards, please inform us and we will gladly replace it.

www.musicsales.com

WISE PUBLICATIONS
PART OF THE MUSIC SALES GROUP
LONDON / NEW YORK / PARIS / SYDNEY / COPENHAGEN / BERLIN / MADRID / TOKYO

Contents

Relative Tuning

The guitar can be tuned with the aid of pitch pipes or dedicated electronic guitar tuners which are available through your local music dealer. If you do not have a tuning device, you can use relative tuning. Estimate the pitch of the 6th string as near as possible to E or at least a comfortable pitch (not too high, as you might break other strings in tuning up). Then, while checking the various positions on the diagram, place a finger from your left hand on the:

5th fret of the E or 6th string and **tune the open A** (or 5th string) to the note (A)

5th fret of the A or 5th string and **tune the open D** (or 4th string) to the note (D)

5th fret of the D or 4th string and **tune the open G** (or 3rd string) to the note (G)

4th fret of the G or 3rd string and **tune the open B** (or 2nd string) to the note (B)

5th fret of the B or 2nd string and **tune the open E** (or 1st string) to the note (E)

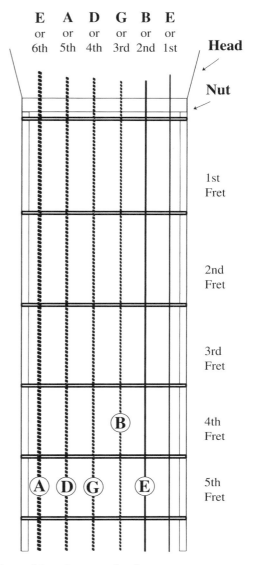

Reading Chord Boxes

Chord boxes are diagrams of the guitar neck viewed head upwards, face on as illustrated. The top horizontal line is the nut, unless a higher fret number is indicated, the others are the frets.

The vertical lines are the strings, starting from E (or 6th) on the left to E (or 1st) on the right.

The black dots indicate where to place your fingers.

Strings marked with an O are played open, not fretted. Strings marked with an X should not be played.

The curved bracket indicates a 'barre' - hold down the strings under the bracket with your first finger, using your other fingers to fret the remaining notes.

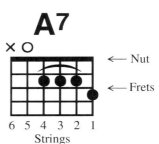

5

Broken Strings

Words & Music by
Nina Woodford, James Morrison & Fraser Thorneycroft-Smith

Capo first fret

Intro | **Fsus2** ‖

Verse 1

      Am
Let me hold you for the last time,

      Fmaj7
It's the last chance to feel again.

      Am   **Fmaj7**   **Dm7**
But you broke me, now I can't feel any - thing.

      Am
When I love you and so untrue,

    Fmaj7
I can't even convince myself.

      Am   **C**   **F**   **Dm7**
When I'm speaking it's the voice of someone else.

Pre-chorus 1

    (Dm7) F **G** **Am***
Oh, it tears me up,

    F   **G**   **Em**
I tried to hold on but it hurts too much.

    F   **G**   **Em**
I tried to for - give but it's not enough,

     F
To make it all O.K.

Chorus 1

Em   Dm7   Am
You can't play our broken strings,

            C   G
You can't feel any - thing,

            Dm7   Am
That your heart don't want to feel.

        C   G
I can't tell you something that ain't real.

        F   Am
Oh, the truth hurts and lies worse,

C   G
How can I give any - more,

          Dm7   Am   G
When I love you a little less than be - fore?

Verse 2

       (G)   Am
Oh, what are we doing?

           Fmaj7
We are turning into dust,

         Am   Fmaj7 Dm7
Playing house in the ruins of us.

         Am
Running back through the fire,

           Fmaj7
When there's nothing left to save.

         Am   C
It's like chasing the very last train,

            F   Dm7
When it's too late, too late.

Pre-chorus 2   As Pre-chorus 1

Chorus 2   As Chorus 1

Bridge 1

       (G)   F   Am
But we're running through the fire,

             C   F
When there's nothing left to save.

            Am
It's like chasing the very last train,

            C   Em
When we both know it's too late, too late.

Chorus 3

(Em)   Dm7   Am
You can't play our broken strings,

           C   G
You can't feel any - thing,

           Dm7   Am
That your heart don't want to feel.

          C   G
I can't tell you something that ain't real.

         F   Am
Oh, the truth hurts and lies worse,

C   G
How can I give any - more,

       Dm7   Am   G
When I love you a little less than be - fore?

                 Dm7   Am   G
Oh, you know that I love you a little less than be - fore.

Outro

(G)   Am   C
Let me hold you for the last time,

         G   F
It's the last chance to feel a - gain.

Cape Cod Kwassa Kwassa

Words & Music by
Christopher Baio, Rostam Batmanglij, Ezra Koenig & Christopher Tomson

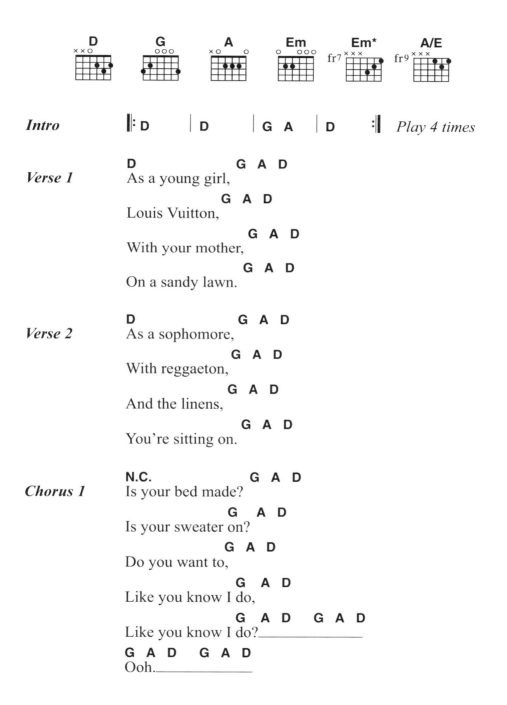

| D | G | A | Em | Em* | A/E |

Intro   ‖: D | D | G A | D :‖ *Play 4 times*

Verse 1

D   G A D
As a young girl,

     G A D
Louis Vuitton,

      G A D
With your mother,

     G A D
On a sandy lawn.

Verse 2

D   G A D
As a sophomore,

     G A D
With reggaeton,

     G A D
And the linens,

     G A D
You're sitting on.

Chorus 1

N.C.   G A D
Is your bed made?

     G A D
Is your sweater on?

    G A D
Do you want to,

    G A D
Like you know I do,

    G A D G A D
Like you know I do?_____

G A D G A D
Ooh._____

Bridge 1

(D)   **Em**
But this feels so unnatural,

A   **D**
    Peter Gabriel too.

         Em*
But this feels so unnatural,

A/E
    Peter Gabriel.

Link 1 ‖: D | D | G   A | D   :‖ *Play 3 times*

Verse 3

(D)   **G   A   D**
Can you stay up,

        G   A   D
To see the dawn,

      G   A   D
In the colours,

      G   A   D
Of Benetton?

Link 2 | D | D | D | D   ‖

Chorus 2

N.C.   **G   A   D**
Is your bed made?

      G   A   D
Is your sweater on?

     G   A   D
Do you want to,

   G   A   D
Like you know I do,

       G   A   D   G   A   D
Like you know I do?_____

G   A   D   G   A   D
Ooh._____

Bridge 2

Em
Feels so unnatural,

A   **D**
    Peter Gabriel too.

         Em*
But this feels so unnatural,

A/E
    Peter Gabriel.

Link 3 ‖ D | D | G A | D   ‖

Interlude ‖: D | D | D | D |

| G | G | G | G |

| D | D | D | D |

| A | A | A | A   :‖

Chorus 3

    N.C.   G A D
Is your bed made?

                    G A D
Is your sweater on?

              G A D
Do you want to,

              G A D
Like you know I do,

              G A D G A D
Like you know I do?_____

G A D G A D
Ooh._____

Outro ‖: G A | D | G A | D   :‖

13

Cheat On Me

Words & Music by
Johnny Marr, Gary Jarman,
Ross Jarman & Ryan Jarman

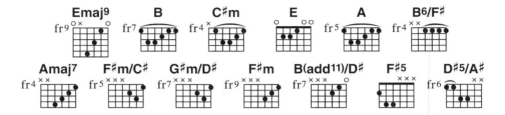

Intro

| Emaj9 | Emaj9 | B | C#m |
| E | E | B | C#m |
| A | A | A | A B ‖

Verse 1

C#m   B6/F#   C#m   B6/F#
I could be someone else   if you'd rather,

C#m   B6/F#   C#m   B6/F#
   Try to win you over like a new   step - father.

C#m   B6/F#   C#m   B6/F#
   Smart but still a sucker for   whoever asks you,

C#m   F#m/C# G#m/D# F#m
   I've pictured the scene,

              C#m   B(add11)/D#   (Amaj7)
So you don't have to spell it out for me.

Bridge

Amaj7   B   Amaj7
'Cause things go to - gether better than others,

              B   F#5   (E)
Like manic de - pression and hypersexuali - ty.

Chorus 1

  E B   C♯m   E
That's an - other,

  B   C♯m
That's an - other,

  A   B E
Cheat on me, cheat on me,⎯ yeah.

  B   C♯m   E
That's an - other,

  B   C♯m
That's an - other,

  A   B (C♯)
Cheat on me, cheat on me,⎯ yeah.

Verse 2

  C♯m   F♯m/C♯ G♯/D♯ F♯   C♯m
  Give it up   without a thought,

    B(add11)/D♯   C♯m   F♯m/C♯ G♯m/D♯ F♯m
And then you'll be the cho - sen   one,

                 C♯m   B(add11)/D♯   (Amaj7)
Through which your friends live vicarious - ly.

Bridge 2

  Amaj7   B   Amaj7
'Cause things go to - gether better than others,

              B   F♯5   (E)
Like manic de - pression and hypersexuali - ty.

Chorus 2   As Chorus 1

Outro

C♯m	A	C♯m	A D♯5/A♯
C♯m	A	C♯m	A D♯5/A♯
C♯m	A D5♯/A♯	C♯m	

15

Crack The Shutters

Words & Music by
Paul Wilson, Gary Lightbody,
Jonathan Quinn, Nathan Connolly & Tom Simpson

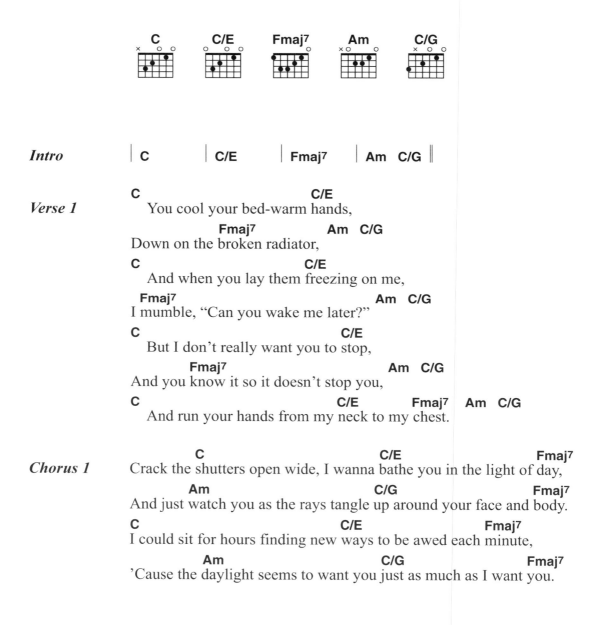

Intro
| C | C/E | Fmaj⁷ | Am C/G ‖

Verse 1

C   C/E
You cool your bed-warm hands,

                  Fmaj⁷   Am C/G
Down on the broken radiator,

C   C/E
And when you lay them freezing on me,

      Fmaj⁷   Am C/G
I mumble, "Can you wake me later?"

C   C/E
But I don't really want you to stop,

        Fmaj⁷   Am C/G
And you know it so it doesn't stop you,

C   C/E   Fmaj⁷   Am C/G
And run your hands from my neck to my chest.

Chorus 1

                C   C/E   Fmaj⁷
Crack the shutters open wide, I wanna bathe you in the light of day,

              Am   C/G   Fmaj⁷
And just watch you as the rays tangle up around your face and body.

C   C/E   Fmaj⁷
I could sit for hours finding new ways to be awed each minute,

           Am   C/G   Fmaj⁷
'Cause the daylight seems to want you just as much as I want you.

Verse 2

C   C/E
It's been minutes, it's been days,

        Fmaj⁷   Am C/G
It's been all I will remember.

C   C/E   Fmaj⁷   Am C/G
Happy lost in your hair and the cold side of the pillow.

C   C/E   Fmaj⁷   Am C/G
Your hills and val - leys are mapped by my intrepid fingers,

C   C/E N.C.
And in a naked slum - ber, I dream all this again.

Chorus 2   As Chorus 1

Chorus 3

          C   C/E   Fmaj⁷
Crack the shutters open wide, I wanna bathe you in the light of day,

          Am   C/G   Fmaj⁷
And just watch you as the rays tangle up around your face and body.

C   C/E   Fmaj⁷
I could sit for hours finding new ways to be awed each minute,

          Am   C/G   Fmaj⁷ C
'Cause the daylight seems to want you just as much as I want you.

Daddy's Gone

Words & Music by
James Allan

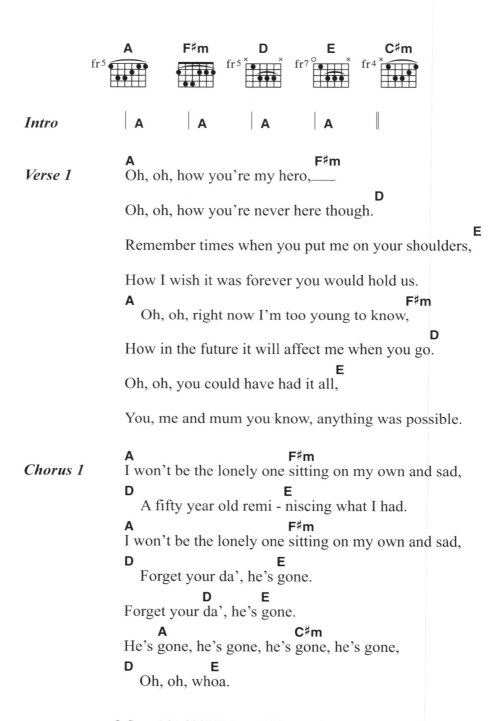

Intro | A | A | A | A   ‖

Verse 1
A   F#m
Oh, oh, how you're my hero,____

                                                      D
Oh, oh, how you're never here though.

                                                                        E
Remember times when you put me on your shoulders,

How I wish it was forever you would hold us.
A   F#m
  Oh, oh, right now I'm too young to know,

                                                      D
How in the future it will affect me when you go.

                                            E
Oh, oh, you could have had it all,

You, me and mum you know, anything was possible.

Chorus 1
A   F#m
I won't be the lonely one sitting on my own and sad,
D   E
  A fifty year old remi - niscing what I had.
A   F#m
I won't be the lonely one sitting on my own and sad,
D   E
  Forget your da', he's gone.
                    D   E
Forget your da', he's gone.
                        A   C#m
He's gone, he's gone, he's gone, he's gone,
D   E
  Oh, oh, whoa.

Verse 2

A   F♯m
All I wanted was a kick-about in the park,

                                                    D
For you to race me home when it was nearly getting dark.

                                    E
How I could've been yours, and you'd be mine,

                                       A
It could've been me and you until the end of time.

                              F♯m
Oh, do what you want, when you want,

                           D
Be as a-fucking insincere as you can.

What kind of way is that to treat your wife,

  E
To see your son on Saturdays,

What way is that to live your life?

Chorus 2

A   F♯m
I won't be the lonely one sitting on my own and sad,

D   E
A fifty year old remi - niscing what I had.

A   F♯m
I won't be the lonely one sitting on my own and sad,

D   E
Forget your da', he's gone,

          D   E
Forget your da', he's gone.

     A   C♯m
He's gone, he's gone, he's gone, he's gone,

D   E
Oh, oh, whoa.

     A   C♯m
He's gone, he's gone, he's gone, he's gone,

D   E
Oh, oh, whoa.

Bridge

A   F♯m
Oh, la, la, la, la.

   D
La, la, la, la.

   E
La, la, la, la.

    A
Ooh.___

F♯m
La, la, la, la.
D
La, la, la, la.
E
La, la, la, la.

Ooh.

Chorus 3

A   **F♯m**
I won't be the lonely one sitting on my own and sad,
D   **E**
 A fifty year old remi - niscing what I had.
A   **F♯m**
I won't be the lonely one sitting on my own and sad,
D   **E**
 Forget your da', he's gone,
     D **E**
Forget your da', he's gone.
   A   **C♯m**
He's gone, he's gone, he's gone, he's gone,
D   **E**
Oh, oh, oh.___
   A   **C♯m**
He's gone, he's gone, he's gone, he's gone,
D   **E**
Oh, oh, oh.___
   A   **C♯m**
He's gone, he's gone, he's gone, he's gone,
D   **E**
 Oh, oh, whoa.
   A   **C♯m**
He's gone, he's gone, he's gone, he's gone,
D   **E**
 Oh, oh, whoa.
  A   **C♯m**   **D** **E**
Oh, he's gone, he's gone, he's gone, he's gone,___
   A   **C♯m**
He's gone, he's gone, he's gone, he's gone,
D   **E** **A**
 Oh, oh, whoa, oh.

Glasvegas

Daniel

Words & Music by
Natasha Khan

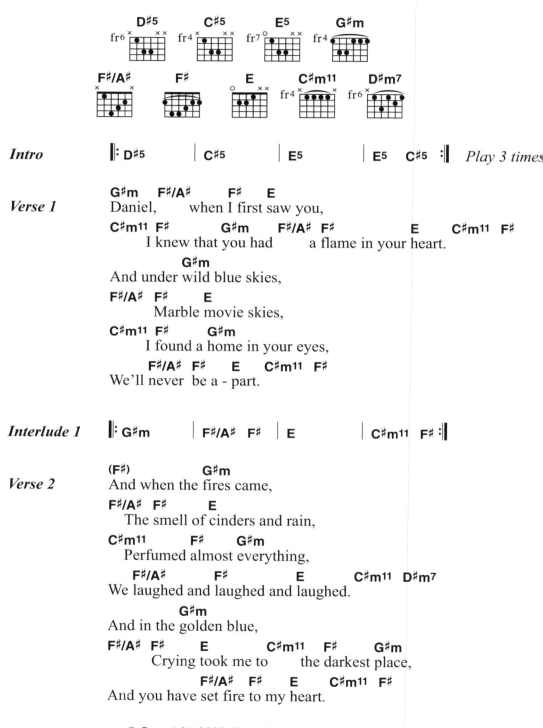

Intro ‖: D♯5 | C♯5 | E5 | E5 C♯5 :‖ *Play 3 times*

Verse 1

G♯m   F♯/A♯   F♯   E
Daniel,   when I first saw you,

C♯m11 F♯   G♯m   F♯/A♯ F♯   E   C♯m11 F♯
    I knew that you had   a flame in your heart.

    G♯m
And under wild blue skies,

F♯/A♯ F♯   E
    Marble movie skies,

C♯m11 F♯   G♯m
    I found a home in your eyes,

    F♯/A♯ F♯   E   C♯m11 F♯
We'll never be a - part.

Interlude 1 ‖: G♯m | F♯/A♯ F♯ | E | C♯m11 F♯ :‖

Verse 2

(F♯)   G♯m
And when the fires came,

F♯/A♯ F♯   E
    The smell of cinders and rain,

C♯m11   F♯   G♯m
    Perfumed almost everything,

    F♯/A♯   F♯   E   C♯m11 D♯m7
We laughed and laughed and laughed.

      G♯m
And in the golden blue,

F♯/A♯ F♯   E   C♯m11 F♯   G♯m
    Crying took me to   the darkest place,

      F♯/A♯ F♯   E   C♯m11 F♯
And you have set fire to my heart.

Chorus 1

G♯m   F♯/A♯   F♯   E   C♯m11   F♯/A♯
When I run   in the dark,___ Dan - iel,

      G♯m   F♯/A♯   F♯   E   C♯m11   D♯m7
In - to a place that's vast,___ Dan - iel.

          G♯m   F♯/A♯   F♯   E   C♯m11   D♯m7
Under a sheet of rain   in my heart,___ Dan - iel,

G♯m   F♯/A♯   F♯   E   C♯m11   F♯
I   dream   of home.

Interlude 2

‖: G♯m | F♯/A♯   F♯ | E | C♯m11   F♯ :‖

Verse 3

(F♯)   G♯m
But in a goodbye bed,

F♯/A♯   F♯   E
   With my arms a - round your neck,

C♯m11   F♯   G♯m
   In - to our mouths the tears crept,

      F♯/A♯   F♯   E   C♯m11   D♯m7
Just kids in the eye of the storm.

          G♯m
And as my house swung round,

F♯/A♯   F♯   E
   My dreams pulled me from the ground,

C♯m11   F♯   G♯m
   For - ever to search for the flame,

    F♯/A♯   F♯   E   C♯m11   F♯
For home a - gain, for home again.

Chorus 2   As Chorus 1

Chorus 3   As Chorus 1

Outro

‖: G♯m | F♯/A♯   F♯ | E | C♯m11   F♯ :‖ *Repeat to fade*

Dog Days Are Over

Words & Music by
Florence Welch & Isabella Summers

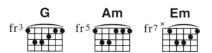

Intro | G | G | G | G |

| G | Am | Em | Em   ‖

Verse 1

G
    Happiness hit her like a train on a track,_____ **Am Em**

G
Coming towards her, stuck still no turning back._____ **Am Em**

    G
She hid around corners and she hid under beds,

        Am   **Em**
She killed it with kiss - es and from it she fled.

    G
With every bubble she sank with her drink,

       Am   **Em**
And washed it a - way down the kitchen sink.

Chorus 1

   G
The dog days are over,

The dog days are done.

    Am
The horses are coming,

  Em
So you better run.

Verse 2
      G
Run fast for your mother, run fast for your father,

Run for your children, for your sisters and brothers.
              Am
Leave all your loving, your loving behind,
      Em
You can't carry it with you if you want to survive.

Chorus 2
      G
The dog days are over,

The dog days are done.
            Am
Can you hear the hor - ses?
    Em   **G**
'Cause here they come.

Verse 3
G   **Am**   **Em**
And I never wanted anything from you,
      G   **Am**   **Em**
Except everything you had and what was left after that too, oh.
G   **Am Em**
   Happiness hit her like a bullet in the head,_____
G
   Struck from a great height,
             Am   **Em**
By someone who should know bet - ter than   that.

Chorus 3   As Chorus 2

Verse 4   As Verse 2

Chorus 4

       G
The dog days are over,

The dog days are done.

              Am
Can you hear the hors - es?

  Em
'Cause here they come.

Chorus 5

       G
The dog days are over,

            Em
The dog days are done.

       G
The horses are coming,

  Am   **Em**
So you better run.

Chorus 6

       G
The dog days are over,

  Am   **Em**
The dog days are done.

   G
The horses are coming,

  Am   **Em** **G**
So you better run._____

Florence And The Machine

Don't Upset The Rhythm

Words & Music by
George Astasio, Jason Pebworth,
James Morrison, Shingai Shoniwa & Daniel Smith

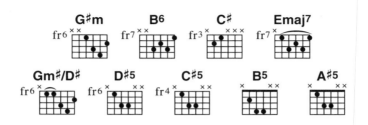

Intro

G♯m B6
Don't upset the rhythm, no,

G♯m B6
Don't upset the rhythm.

G♯m B6
Don't upset the rhythm, no,

G♯m B6
Don't upset the rhythm.

Verse 1

G♯m   B6
The time is right, the sun is sleeping in the sky,

G♯m   B6
Free your mind, you never know what you might find.

C♯
What's your vice? You know we won't compromise,

G♯m   B6
So let me show you something super beautiful.

G♯m   B6
Let's rock the boat, the magic is unstoppable.

G♯m   B6
Four on the floor, it's the rhythm you've been waiting for.

C♯
Pure delight, kick, snare, hat, ride.

Pre-chorus 1

G♯m   B6   Emaj7
It's all up to you and whatever you do,

              G♯m/D♯ D♯5 C♯5 B5 A♯5
Don't cut into my action,   four, three, two, one.

Chorus 1

G♯m
(Go baby, go baby go.)

B6
Don't upset the rhythm, no.

G♯m
(Go baby, go baby go.)

B6
Don't upset the rhythm.

G♯m
(Go baby, go baby go.)

B6   G♯m
Don't upset the rhythm, don't you dare.

(Go baby, go baby go.)

B6
Don't upset the rhythm.

Verse 2

G♯m   B6
  Skin and bone and a baton microphone,

G♯m   B6
  Can't get home, but you can use my dog and bone.

G♯m   B6
  We'll crank that stereo even when the speakers blow,

C♯
  D-I-Y, just meet me up in paradise.

Pre-chorus 2

G♯m   Emaj7
Whatever it takes to carry you a - way,

                          G♯m/D♯   D♯5 C♯5 B5 A♯5
It all comes down to actions,   four, three, two, one.

Chorus 2   As Chorus 1

Interlude   ‖: C♯ | C♯ | C♯ | C♯ :‖

Pre-chorus 3

G#m
Go baby, go baby go.

B6
Go baby, go baby go,

This time I like it.

Emaj7
Go baby, go baby go,

                G#m/D#
Now don't you dare,

D#5   **C#5**   **B5**   **A#5**
Don't up - set the rhy - thm.

Chorus 3

G#m
  No,

Don't upset the rhythm, no.

B6
(Go, go, go.)

Don't upset the rhythm.

Emaj7
(Go, go, go.)

                          G#m/D#
Don't upset the rhythm, don't you dare,

         D#5   **C#5**   **B5** **A#5**
I told you, don't up - set the rhy - thm.

Chorus 4

G#m
(Go baby, go baby go.)

Don't upset the rhythm, no.

B6
(Go baby, go baby go.)

Don't upset the rhythm.

Emaj7
(Go baby, go baby go.)

                        G#m/D#
Don't upset the rhythm, don't you dare.

D#5   **C#5**   **B5**   **A#5**
Don't up - set the rhy - thm.

Chorus 5

G♯m
(Go baby, go baby go.)

Don't upset the rhythm, no.
B⁶
(Go baby, go baby go.)

Don't upset the rhythm.
Emaj⁷
(Go baby, go baby go.)

                                G♯m/D♯
Don't upset the rhythm, don't you dare.
D♯5 C♯5 B5 A♯5
            Hey,

Chorus 6

G♯m
(Go baby, go baby go.)

Don't upset the rhythm, no.
B⁶
(Go baby, go baby go.)

Don't upset the rhythm.
Emaj⁷
(Go baby, go baby go.)

                                  G♯m/D♯
Don't upset the rhythm, don't you dare.
D♯5   **C♯5**   **B5**   **A♯5**   **G♯m**
Don't up - set the rhy - thm.

Falling Down

Words & Music by
Noel Gallagher

Em   Em7   Em(♭6)   A7sus2   A7sus2/4

G   D6/F♯   Cmaj7   D6sus2   E5   fr7

Capo 2nd fret

Intro ‖: Em | Em7 | Em(♭6) | A7sus2 :‖

Verse 1

Em   Em7
The summer sun, it blows my mind,
Em(♭6)   A7sus2
Is falling down on all that I've ever known.
Em   Em7
In time we'll kiss the world goodbye,
Em(♭6)   A7sus2
Falling down on all that I've ever known,
Em(♭6)   A7sus2/4
Is all that I've ever known.

‖: Em | Em7 | Em(♭6) | A7sus2 :‖

Verse 2

Em   Em7
A dying scream makes no sound,
Em(♭6)   A7sus2
Calling out to   all that I've ever known.
Em   Em7
And here am I,   lost and found,
Em(♭6)   A7sus2/4
Calling out to   all.
Em   Em7   Em(♭6)   A7sus2
We live a dying dream,
Em   Em7
If you know what I mean.
Em(♭6)   A7sus2
In all that I've ever known,
Em(♭6)   A7sus2/4
It's all that I've ever known.

Instr. | Em | Em | Em | Em |

Bridge 1

G   D6/F♯   Em
Catch the wheel that breaks the butterfly,

Cmaj7   Em
A cry, the rain that fills the ocean wide.

G   D6/F♯   Em
I tried to talk with God to no avail,

Em   Cmaj7   D6sus2
    I call him up in   and out of nowhere.

Cmaj7   A7sus2   G
I said if you won't save me, please don't waste my time.

Instr. | Em | Em7 | Em(♭6) | A7sus2 |

‖: Em | Em7 | Em(♭6) | A7sus2 :‖

| Em | Em7 |

Em(♭6)   A7sus2
It's all that I've ever known,

Cmaj7   D6sus2
It's all that I've ever known.

‖: E5 | E5 | E5 | E5 :‖

Play 4 times

Bridge 2 As Bridge 1

Instr. ‖: Em | Em7 | Em(♭6) | A7sus2 :‖

Verse 1

Em   Em7
The summer sun, it blows my mind,

Em(♭6)   A7sus2
Is falling down on all that I've ever known.

Em   Em7
In time we'll kiss the world goodbye,

Em(♭6)   A7sus2
Falling down on all that I've ever known,

Em(♭6)   A7sus2/4 | A7sus2/4 ‖
    Is all that I've ever known.

Farewell To The Fairground

Words & Music by
Harry McVeigh, Charles Cave & Jack Brown

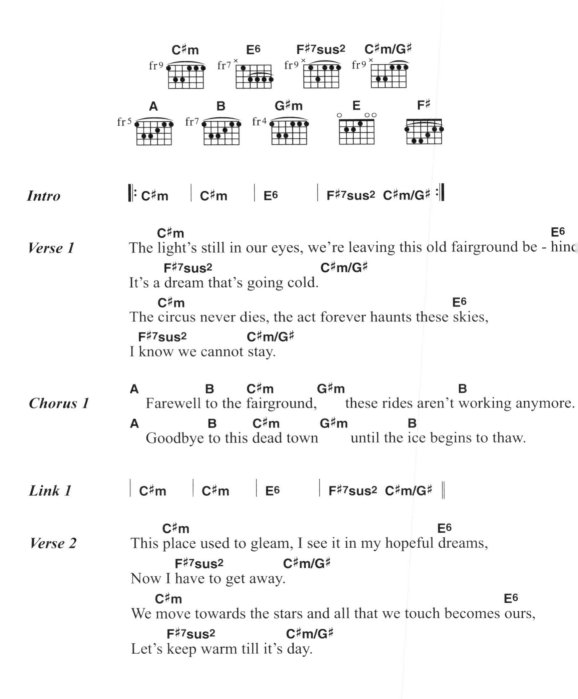

Intro   ‖: C#m | C#m | E6 | F#7sus2 C#m/G# :‖

Verse 1
     C#m   **E6**
The light's still in our eyes, we're leaving this old fairground be - hind
     F#7sus2   **C#m/G#**
It's a dream that's going cold.
     C#m   **E6**
The circus never dies, the act forever haunts these skies,
  F#7sus2   **C#m/G#**
I know we cannot stay.

Chorus 1
  A   **B**   **C#m**   **G#m**   **B**
  Farewell to the fairground,   these rides aren't working anymore.
  A   **B**   **C#m**   **G#m**   **B**
  Goodbye to this dead town   until the ice begins to thaw.

Link 1 | C#m | C#m | E6 | F#7sus2 C#m/G# ‖

Verse 2
     C#m   **E6**
This place used to gleam, I see it in my hopeful dreams,
      F#7sus2   **C#m/G#**
Now I have to get away.
     C#m   **E6**
We move towards the stars and all that we touch becomes ours,
     F#7sus2   **C#m/G#**
Let's keep warm till it's day.

Chorus 2   As Chorus 1

Bridge 1

      A   B   C♯m

We'll head south, just hold my hand now.

    G♯m   B

I feel like I'm casting off my clothes.

            A   B   C♯m

And I'm running through the snow to - wards the sunset,

         G♯m   B

And I'm always with you.

Middle   ‖: E | E | B | C♯m :‖

               E

‖: Keep on running, keep, keep on running,

           B   C♯m

There's no place like home, there's no place like home. :‖ *Play 4 times*

E

    Keep on running, keep, keep on running,

        F♯   G♯m

There's no place like home, there's no place like home.

E

    Keep on running, keep, keep on running,

        F♯   G♯m

There's no place like home, there's no place like home.

Chorus 3   As Chorus 1

Bridge 2   As Bridge 1

Outro   ‖: A B | C♯ | G♯m | B   :‖ *Play 4 times*

    | C♯m | C♯m | C♯m | C♯m | C♯m ‖

The Fear

Words & Music by
Lily Allen & Greg Kurstin

F   F/E♭   B♭/D   B♭m/D♭   Dm   Am   E♭

Intro | F | F/E♭ | B♭/D | B♭m/D♭ ‖

Verse 1

F   F/E♭   B♭/D
I want to be rich and I want lots of money,
                   B♭m/D♭   F
I don't care about clever, I don't care about funny.
                    F/E♭   B♭/D
I want loads of clothes and fuckloads of diamonds,
                  B♭m/D♭   F
I heard people die while they are trying to find them.

Verse 2

F   F/E♭   B♭/D
And I'll take my clothes off and it will be shameless,
              B♭m/D♭   F
'Cause everyone knows that's how you get famous.
                   F/E♭   B♭/D
I'll look at the sun and I'll look in the mirror,
                 B♭m/D♭   F
I'm on the right track yeah, I'm on to a winner.

Chorus 1

F   Dm   Am
I don't know what's right and what's   real anymore,
F   Dm   E♭
And I don't know how I'm meant to feel anymore.
F   Dm   Am
And when we think it will all become   clear,
F   Dm   E♭
'Cause I'm being taken over by the fear.

| *Link 1* | | F | | F/E♭ | | B♭/D | | B♭m/D♭ ‖ |

Verse 3
F   F/E♭   B♭/D
   Life's about film stars and less about mothers,
             B♭m/D♭   F
It's all about fast cars and cussing each other.
           F/E♭   B♭/D
But it doesn't matter cause I'm packing plastic,
           B♭m/D♭   F
And that's what makes my life so fucking fan - tastic.

Verse 4
F   F/E♭   B♭/D
And I am a weapon of massive con - sumption,
          B♭m/D♭   F
And it's not my fault it's how I'm programmed to function.
         F/E♭   B♭/D
I'll look at the sun and I'll look in the mirror,
         B♭m/D♭   F
I'm on the right track yeah, I'm on to a winner.

Chorus 2   As Chorus 1

| *Link 2* | ‖: F | | F/E♭ | | B♭/D | | B♭m/D♭ :‖ |

Verse 5
F   F/E♭   B♭/D
   Forget about guns and forget ammu - nition,
            B♭m/D♭   F
'Cause I'm killing them all on my own little mission.
         F/E♭   B♭/D
Now I'm not a saint, but I'm not a sinner,
         B♭m/D♭   F
Now everything's cool as long as I'm getting thinner.

Chorus 3   As Chorus 1

| *Outro* | | F | | Dm | | Am | | Am | | |
| | | F | | Dm | | Am | | E♭ | | ‖ |

5 Years Time

Words & Music by
Charlie Fink

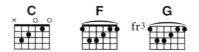

Intro ‖: C F │ G F │ C F │ G F :‖ C ‖

‖: C F │ G F │ C F │ G F :‖

Verse 1

(F)   C   F   G   F
Oh, well in five years time we could be walking round a zoo,
          C   F   G   F
With the sun shining down over me and you.
              C   F   G   F
And there'll be love in the bodies of the elephants too,
                      C   F   G   F
And I'll put my hands over your eyes, but you'll peep through.

Chorus 1

(F)   C   F G
And there'll be sun, sun, sun,
                      F
All over our bodies.
        C   F G
And sun, sun, sun,
                  F
All down our necks.
              C   F G
And there'll be sun, sun, sun,
                  F
All over our faces,
        C   F G
And sun, sun, sun,
                  F
So what the heck.

Verse 2

   (F)   **C**   **F** **G**   **F**
'Cause I'll be laughing at all your silly little jokes,

         C   **F** **G**   **F**
And we'll be laughing about how we used to smoke,

       C   **F**   **G**   **F**
All those stupid little cigarettes and drink stupid wine,

        C   **F**   **G**   **F**
'Cause it's what we needed to have a good time.

Chorus 2

   (F)   **C**   **F** **G**
But it was fun, fun, fun,

         F
When we were drinking.

     C   **F** **G**
It was fun, fun, fun,

         F
When we were drunk.

       C   **F** **G**
And it was fun, fun, fun,

         F
When we were laughing,

     C   **F** **G**
It was fun, fun, fun,

       F
Oh, it was fun.

Link 1 | **C** **F** | **G** **F** | **C** **F** | **G** **F** ‖

Verse 3

   (F)   **C**   **F**   **G**   **F**
Oh, well I look at you and say: "It's the happiest that I've ever been,"

         C   **F**   **G**   **F**
And I'll say: "I no longer feel I have to be James Dean."

          C   **F** **G**   **F**
And she'll say: "Yeah, well, I feel all pretty happy too,

       C   **F**   **G**   **F**
And I'm always pretty happy when I'm just kicking back with you."

Chorus 3

(F)   C   F   G
And it'll be love, love, love,

            F
All through our bodies.

    C   F   G
And love, love, love,

         F
All through our minds.

        C   F   G
And it'll be love, love, love,

         F
All over her face.

    C   F   G
And love, love, love,

      F
All over mine.

Verse 4

(F)   C   F   G   F
Although maybe all these moments are just in my head,

      C   F   G   F
I'll be thinking 'bout them as I'm lying in bed.

        C   F   G   F
And you know that it be - lieve, it might not really come true,

          C   F   G   F
But in my mind I'm having a pretty good time with you, oh.

Bridge 1

      C   F G   F
In five years time   I might not know you,

      C   F G   F
In five years time   we might not speak.

        C   F G   F
Oh, in five years time   we might not get along,

      C   F G   F   (C)
In five years time   you might just prove me wrong.

Link 2 | C F | G F | C F | G F ‖

Chorus 4
           (F)   **C**   **N.C.**
Oh, there'll be love,   love, love,

Wherever you go.

There'll be love, love, love,

Wherever you go.
          C   **F**
There'll be love, love, love,
G   **F**
Wherever you go.
          C   **F**
There'll be love, love, love,
N.C.
Wherever you go.
          C   **F**   **G**
There'll be love, love, love,
          F
Wherever you go.
          C   **F**   **G**
There'll be love, love, love,
          F
Wherever you go.
          C   **F**   **G**
There'll be love, love, love.
          F
Wherever you go.
          C   **F**   **G**
There'll be love, love, love.
          F   **C**
Wherever you go there'll be love.

The Fix

Words & Music by
Richard Hawley, Guy Garvey,
Richard Jupp, Peter Turner, Mark Potter & Craig Potter

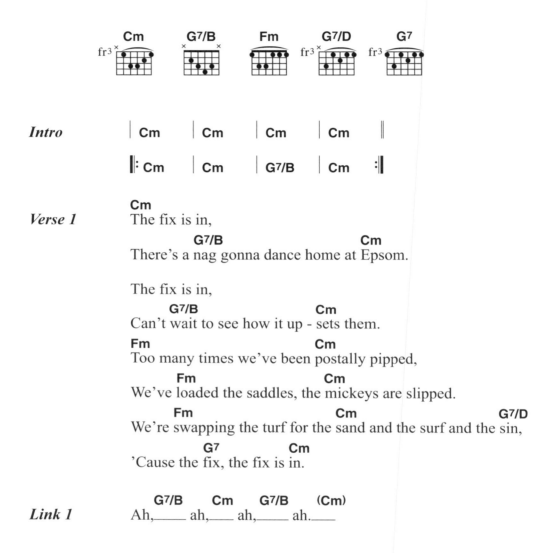

Intro | Cm | Cm | Cm | Cm   ‖

‖: Cm | Cm | G⁷/B | Cm   :‖

Verse 1

Cm
The fix is in,
       G⁷/B   **Cm**
There's a nag gonna dance home at Epsom.

The fix is in,
      G⁷/B   **Cm**
Can't wait to see how it up - sets them.
Fm   **Cm**
Too many times we've been postally pipped,
      Fm   **Cm**
We've loaded the saddles, the mickeys are slipped.
      Fm   **Cm**   **G⁷/D**
We're swapping the turf for the sand and the surf and the sin,
      G⁷   **Cm**
'Cause the fix, the fix is in.

Link 1   **G⁷/B** **Cm** **G⁷/B** **(Cm)**
Ah,____ ah,___ ah,____ ah.____

Verse 2

Cm
The fix is in,

G7/B   Cm
The odds that I got were de - licious.

The fix is in,

G7/B   Cm
The jockey is cocky and vicious.

   Fm   Cm
The re - doubtable beast has had pegasus pills,

   Fm   Cm
We'll buy him the patch in the Tuscany hills.

   Fm   Cm   G7/B
And the Vino de Vici will flow like a river in spring,

   G7   Cm
Now the fix, the fix is in.

Link 2

  G7/B Cm G7/B Cm
Ah,____ ah,____ ah,____ ah.____

  G7/B Cm G7/B Cm
Ah,____ ah,____ ah,____ ah.____

Bridge 1

Fm   Cm
La, la, da, da, la, la, da, da.

Fm   Cm
La, la, da, da, la, la, da, da.

Fm   Cm
La, la, da, da, la, la, da, da.

G7/D G7
La.____

Verse 3

     Cm
The fix is in,

     G⁷/D   **Cm**
The snaps of the steward so candid.

The fix is in,

        G⁷/B   **Cm**
Yes, our pigeons have finally landed.

    Fm   **Cm**
The Donoghue sisters will meet us in France,

    Fm   **Cm**
In penguins and pearls, we'll drink and we'll dance,

     Fm   **Cm**   **G⁷/D**
Till the end of our days, 'cause it ain't left to chance that we win.

     G⁷   **Cm**
'Cause the fix, the fix is in.

Link 3

    G⁷/B   **Cm**   **G⁷/B**   **(Cm)**
Ah,____ ah,____ ah,____ ah.____

    G⁷/B   **Cm**   **G⁷/B**   **(Cm)**
Ah,____ ah,____ ah,____ ah.____

| **G⁷/B** | **Cm** | **G⁷/B** | **Cm** | |

| **G⁷/B** | **Cm** | **G⁷/B** | **Cm** | **Cm** ‖

Outro

Fm   **Cm**
La, la, da, da, la, la, da, da.

Fm   **Cm**
La, la, da, da, la, la, da, da.

Fm   **Cm**
La, la, da, da, la, la, da, da.

G⁷/D **G⁷** **Cm**
La.____

For What It's Worth

Words & Music by
William Lloyd, Brian Molko, Stefan Olsdal & Steven Forrest

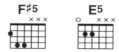

Tune guitar down a semitone

Intro ‖: F♯5 | F♯5 E5 | F♯5 | F♯5 E5 :‖

Verse 1

F♯5   E5 F♯5
　The end of the century,　I said my goodbyes,

E5   F♯5
　For what it's worth,

                              E5 F♯5
I always aim to please,　　but I nearly died.

E5   F♯5
　For what it's worth,

                              E5 F♯5
Come on lay with me,　　'cause I'm on fire.

E5   F♯5
　For what it's worth,

                              E5 F♯5 N.C.
I tear the sun in three,　　to light up your eyes.

Chorus 1

N.C.   F♯5
For what it's　worth.

For what it's worth.

              E5
For what it's　worth.

              F♯5
For what it's　worth.

Verse 2

F♯5   E5 F♯5

Broke up the family,   everybody cried.

E5   F♯5

  For what it's worth,

                         E5 F♯5

I have a slow disease   that sucked me dry.

E5   F♯5

  For what it's worth,

                        E5 F♯5

Come on walk with me   into the rising tide.

E5   F♯5

  For what it's worth,

                   E5 F♯5 N.C.

Filled a cavity,   your God-shaped hole tonight.

Chorus 2

N.C.   F♯5

For what it's   worth.

For what it's worth.

            E5

For what it's   worth.

            F♯5

For what it's   worth.

For what it's worth.

For what it's worth.

            E5

For what it's   worth.

            F♯5

For what it's   worth.

Interlude | N.C.   ‖

Bridge

F#5
No one cares when you're out on the street,

E5 F#5
   Picking up the pieces to make ends meet.

E5
  No one cares when you're down in the gutter,

F#5
Got no friends, got no lover.

No one cares when you're out on the street,

E5 F#5
   Picking up the pieces to make ends meet.

E5
  No one cares when you're down in the gutter,

F#5 N.C.
Got no friends, got no lover.

Chorus 3

N.C.   F#5
For what it's   worth, got no lover.

For what it's worth, got no lover.

        E5
For what it's   worth, got no lover.

        F#5
For what it's   worth, got no lover.

For what it's worth, got no lover.

For what it's worth, got no lover.

        E5
For what it's   worth, got no lover.

F#5 N.C.
Got no friends, got no lover.

Geraldine

Words & Music by
James Allan

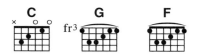

Intro ‖: C | C G | F | F G :‖ *Play 4 times*

Verse 1
       C   G F
    When your sparkle evades your soul,

                         G C
I'll be at your side to console.

                                   G F
When you're standing on the window ledge,

                         G C
I'll talk you back, back from the edge.

                     G F
I will turn, I will turn your tide,

                             G C
Be your shepherd I swear, be your guide.

                                         G   F
When you're lost in your deep and darkest place a - round,

                                 G C
May my words walk with you home safe and sound.

Link 1
C   G   F G
Ooh, ooh,___ ooh.
C   G   F G
Ooh, ooh,___ ooh.

Verse 2

C   G F
When you say that I'm no good and you feel like walk - ing,

                     G   C
I need to make sure you know it's just the prescription talking.

                  G F
When your feet decide to walk you on the wayward side,

                 G C
Climbing up upon the stairs and down the downward slide,

        G F
I will turn, I will turn your tide,

          G C
Do all that I can to heal you inside.

            G F
I will be the angel on your shoul - der,

             G   C
My name is Geraldine, I'm your so - cial work - er.

Link 2

C G F G
Ooh, ooh,____ ooh.

C G F G
Ooh, ooh,____ ooh.

Bridge

C G F G C
I see you need me,

 G   F   G
I know you do.____

C G F G C
I see you need me,

 G   F
I know you do.

 G   (C)
I know you do.

Instr.

‖: C | C G | F | F G :‖ *Play 4 times*

Verse 3

C   G F
 I will turn, I will turn your tide,

          G C
Do all that I can to heal you inside.

            G F
I will be the angel on your shoul - der,

           G   C
My name is Geraldine, I'm your so - cial work - er.

Get On Your Boots

Words by Bono
Music by U2

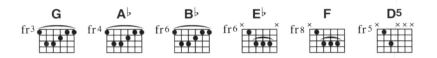

Intro

riff 1

```
      D  C  A  C  A  D   C  A  C  C  A  G  A
   ‖: 5fr 3fr 5fr 3fr 5fr 5fr  3fr 5fr 3fr 3fr 5fr 3fr 5fr :‖  Play 4 times
      ⑤  ⑤  ⑥  ⑤  ⑥  ⑤   ⑤  ⑥  ⑤  ⑤  ⑥  ⑥  ⑥
```

Verse 1

riff 1(N.C.)
Future needs a big kiss, winds blow with a twist,

riff 1
Never seen a moon like this, can you see it too?

riff 1
Night is falling everywhere, rockets at the funfair,

riff 1
Satan loves a bomb scare, but he won't scare you.

Chorus 1

riff 1(N.C.)   **riff 1**
      Hey, sexy boots,

       riff 1
Get on your boots, yeah.

Verse 2

riff 1(N.C.)
 Free me from the dark dream, candy floss, ice cream,

riff 1
All our kids are screaming but the ghosts aren't real.

riff 1
Here's where we gotta be, love and community,

riff 1
Laughter is eternity if joy is real.

Bridge 1

G   A♭   G   A♭
   You don't know how beautiful,

G   B♭   E♭   F   G
   You don't know how beauti - ful you are.

           A♭   G   A♭
You don't know, and you don't get it do you?

G   B♭   E♭   F   riff 1
   You don't know how beauti - ful you are.

Link 1

riff 1(x2)

Verse 3

riff 1(N.C.)
That's someone's stuff they're blowing up, we're into growing up,

riff 1
Women of the future, hold the big revelations.

riff 1
I've got a submarine, you got gasoline,

riff 1
I don't wanna talk about wars between nations.

Chorus 2

riff 1
   Not right now.

     riff 1
Sexy boots, yeah. (No, no, no.)

        riff 1
Get on your boots, yeah. (Not right now.)

    riff 1
Bossy boots.

Bridge 2

G   A♭   G   A♭
   You don't know how beautiful,

G   B♭   E♭   F   G
   You don't know how beauti - ful you are.

           A♭   G   A♭
You don't know, and you don't get it do you?

G   B♭   E♭   F   riff 1(x2)
   You don't know how beauti - ful you are.

Chorus 3
        riff 1
Sexy boots,

I don't wanna talk about wars between nations.
        riff 1
Sexy boots, yeah.

Bridge 3
        N.C.
Let me in the sound, let me in the sound,

Let me in the sound, sound,

Let me in the sound, sound,
           riff 1
Meet me in the sound.
riff 1
Let me in the sound, let me in the sound now,
          riff 1
God I'm going down, I don't wanna drown now,
        riff 1
Meet me in the sound.
riff 1
Let me in the sound, let me in the sound,
        riff 1
Let me in the sound, sound,

Let me in the sound, sound,
        riff 1 *(x2)*
Meet me in the sound.

Chorus 4
        riff 1
Get on your boots,
        riff 1
Get on your boots,
        riff 1
Get on your boots, yeah, hey, hey.
        riff 1
Get on your boots, yeah, hey, hey.
        riff 1
Get on your boots, yeah, hey, hey.
        D5
Get on your boots, yeah, hey, hey.

Gives You Hell

Words & Music by
Tyson Ritter & Nick Wheeler

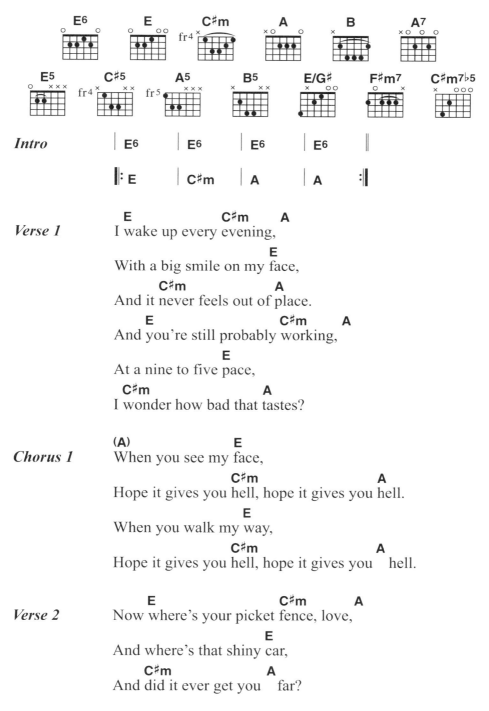

Intro | E6 | E6 | E6 | E6 ||

|: E | C#m | A | A :|

Verse 1
          E   C#m   A
I wake up every evening,
                               E
With a big smile on my face,
         C#m   A
And it never feels out of place.
              E   C#m   A
And you're still probably working,
                    E
At a nine to five pace,
        C#m   A
I wonder how bad that tastes?

Chorus 1
            (A)   E
When you see my face,
                    C#m   A
Hope it gives you hell, hope it gives you hell.
                    E
When you walk my way,
                    C#m   A
Hope it gives you hell, hope it gives you   hell.

Verse 2
              E   C#m   A
Now where's your picket fence, love,
                    E
And where's that shiny car,
         C#m   A
And did it ever get you   far?

cont.

          E   C♯m   A
You never seemed so tense, love,

                           E
I never seen you fall so hard.

C♯m   A
Do you know where you are?

Pre-chorus 1

B   C♯m
Truth be told, I miss you,

    B   A7
And truth be told, I'm lying.

Chorus 2

(A7)   E
When you see my face,

                C♯5   A5
Hope it gives you hell, hope it gives you hell.

                E5
When you walk my way,

                C♯5   A5
Hope it gives you hell, hope it gives you   hell.

            E5   C♯5   A5
If you find a man that's worth a damn and treats you well,

            E5   B5   A5
Then he's a fool, you're just as well, hope it gives you   hell,

            G5   (E)
Hope it gives you hell.

Interlude ‖: E | C♯m | A | A   :‖

Verse 3

          E   C♯m   A
To - morrow you'll be thinking to your - self,

                      E
Yeah, where did it all go wrong?

         C♯m   A
But the list goes on and on.

Pre-chorus 2   As Pre-chorus 1

Chorus 3

(A7)   E5
When you see my face,

                C♯5   A5
Hope it gives you hell, hope it gives you hell.

                E5
When you walk my way,

                C♯5   A5
Hope it gives you hell, hope it gives you   hell.

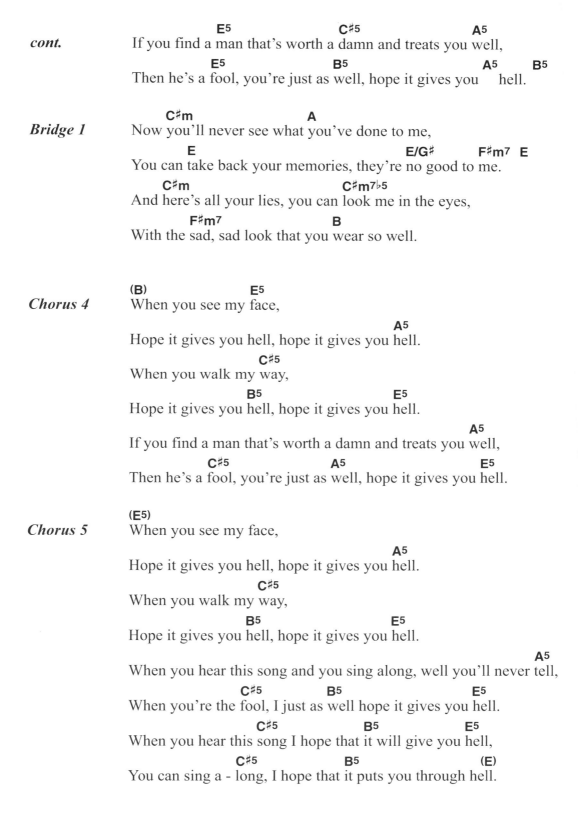

cont.

          E5   C$\sharp$5   A5
If you find a man that's worth a damn and treats you well,

          E5   B5   A5   B5
Then he's a fool, you're just as well, hope it gives you   hell.

Bridge 1

      C$\sharp$m   A
Now you'll never see what you've done to me,

      E   E/G$\sharp$ F$\sharp$m7 E
You can take back your memories, they're no good to me.

      C$\sharp$m   C$\sharp$m7$\flat$5
And here's all your lies, you can look me in the eyes,

      F$\sharp$m7   B
With the sad, sad look that you wear so well.

Chorus 4

      (B)   E5
When you see my face,

                    A5
Hope it gives you hell, hope it gives you hell.

          C$\sharp$5
When you walk my way,

        B5   E5
Hope it gives you hell, hope it gives you hell.

                         A5
If you find a man that's worth a damn and treats you well,

      C$\sharp$5   A5   E5
Then he's a fool, you're just as well, hope it gives you hell.

Chorus 5

      (E5)
When you see my face,

                    A5
Hope it gives you hell, hope it gives you hell.

          C$\sharp$5
When you walk my way,

        B5   E5
Hope it gives you hell, hope it gives you hell.

                             A5
When you hear this song and you sing along, well you'll never tell,

      C$\sharp$5   B5   E5
When you're the fool, I just as well hope it gives you hell.

      C$\sharp$5   B5   E5
When you hear this song I hope that it will give you hell,

      C$\sharp$5   B5   (E)
You can sing a - long, I hope that it puts you through hell.

Golden Age

Words & Music by
David Sitek, David Malone, Gerard Smith,
Jaleel Bunton & Babatunde Adebimpe

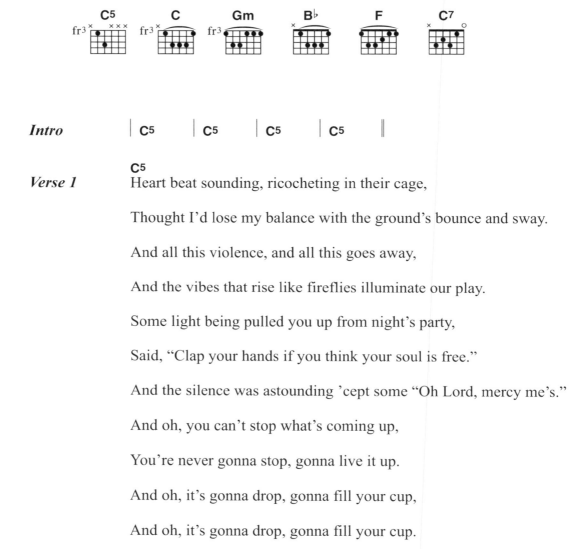

Intro | C5 | C5 | C5 | C5 ‖

Verse 1

C5
Heart beat sounding, ricocheting in their cage,

Thought I'd lose my balance with the ground's bounce and sway.

And all this violence, and all this goes away,

And the vibes that rise like fireflies illuminate our play.

Some light being pulled you up from night's party,

Said, "Clap your hands if you think your soul is free."

And the silence was astounding 'cept some "Oh Lord, mercy me's."

And oh, you can't stop what's coming up,

You're never gonna stop, gonna live it up.

And oh, it's gonna drop, gonna fill your cup,

And oh, it's gonna drop, gonna fill your cup.

Chorus 1

        C   **Gm** **B♭** **F**
The age of miracles,

             C   **Gm** **B♭** **F**
The age of sound.___

              C   **Gm** **B♭** **F**
Well there's a golden age,

          C   **Gm**   **B♭**   **F**
Coming round, coming round, coming round.

Link 1 | **C5** | **C5** | **C5** | **C5**   ‖

Verse 2

C5
Give it up, 'stead of grabbing for decay,

What we viewed as gold, I believe pollutes this space.

And it's grace ascending like a snake up your tree,

Up your happy ending understanding, all you're supposed to be.

Let it move right in, let it kiss your face,

Let it sow your skin in perpetual embrace.

Like I said, "Love's light is laughter."

Like the sun spitting happiness into the hereafter,

Oh, here it comes like a natural disaster,

Ah, blowing up like a ghetto blaster.

Ah, here it comes, bring it faster.

Ah, here it comes, bring it faster!

Chorus 2   As Chorus 1

Bridge

```
     C              F
Love, don't you falter,
          C
Burning hearts dragged behind,
            F
The horses dancing on the altar.
                  C
Hooves breaking gods to diamond dust and stars.
              C7
And there you are.
```

Verse 3

```
          C7
Now we're all allowed to breathe,
            C5
Walls dis - solve with the hunger and the greed.

Move your body, you've got all you need.

And your arms in the air stir a sea of stars,

And oh, here it comes and it's not so far.

All light beings, come on now make haste,

Clap your hands if you think you're in the right place.

Thunder all surrounding,

Oh, feel it quake with the joy resounding.

Palm to the palm, you can feel it pounding,

Never give it up you can feel it mounting.

Oh, it's gonna drop, gonna fill your cup and,

Oh, it's gonna drop, gonna fill your cup.
```

Chorus 3   As Chorus 1

Chorus 4   As Chorus 1

Outro   ‖: C Gm | B♭ F | C Gm | B♭ F :‖

58

Heads Will Roll

Words & Music by
Nicholas Zinner, Brian Chase & Karen Orzolek

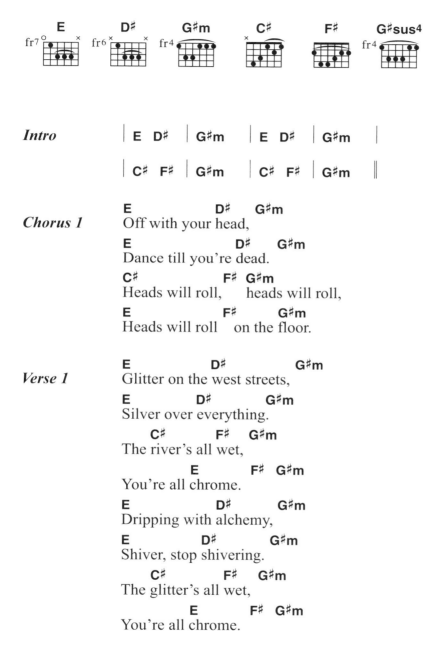

Intro

| E D♯ | G♯m | E D♯ | G♯m |

| C♯ F♯ | G♯m | C♯ F♯ | G♯m ‖

Chorus 1

E   D♯   G♯m
Off with your head,

E   D♯   G♯m
Dance till you're dead.

C♯   F♯ G♯m
Heads will roll,   heads will roll,

E   F♯   G♯m
Heads will roll   on the floor.

Verse 1

E   D♯   G♯m
Glitter on the west streets,

E   D♯   G♯m
Silver over everything.

    C♯   F♯   G♯m
The river's all wet,

        E   F♯ G♯m
You're all chrome.

E   D♯   G♯m
Dripping with alchemy,

E   D♯   G♯m
Shiver, stop shivering.

    C♯   F♯   G♯m
The glitter's all wet,

        E   F♯ G♯m
You're all chrome.

Bridge 1

G♯sus4
The men cry out, the girls cry out,

The men cry out, the girls cry out,

The men cry out, oh no.

The men cry out, the girls cry out,

The men cry out, the girls cry out,

                F♯ C♯ B
The men cry out,   oh no.

Interlude 1

   E D♯ G♯m   E D♯ G♯m
Oh,   oh.

   C♯ F♯ G♯m   E F♯ G♯m
Oh,   oh.

Chorus 2

   E   D♯   G♯m
Off, off with your head,

      E   D♯   G♯m
Dance, dance till you're dead.

C♯   F♯ G♯m
Heads will roll,   heads will roll,

E   F♯   G♯m
Heads will roll   on the floor.

Bridge 2

B   E   G♯m B   E G♯m
You came last,   take the past.

B   E   G♯m C♯ F♯ G♯m
Shut your eyes, re - a - lize.

B   E   G♯m B   E G♯m
You came last,   take the past.

E   D♯ G♯m C♯ F♯ G♯m
Shut your eyes, re - a - lize.

Link

| B E | G♯m | B E | G♯m |

| E D♯ | G♯m | C♯ F♯ | G♯m ‖

Verse 2

E   D♯   G♯m
Glitter on the west streets,

E   D♯   G♯m
Silver over everything.

     C♯   F♯ G♯m
The glitter's all wet,

          E   F♯ G♯m
You're all chrome,

          E   F♯ G♯m
You're all chrome.

Interlude 2

E D♯ G♯m   E D♯ G♯m
      Oh,   oh.

C♯ F♯ G♯m   E F♯ G♯m
      Oh.

Chorus 3

          E   D♯   G♯m
Off, off, off with your head,

             E   D♯ G♯m
Dance, dance, dance till you're dead.

          C♯   F♯   G♯m
Off, off, off with your head,

             E   F♯ G♯m
Dance, dance, dance till you're dead.

          E   D♯ G♯m
Off, off, off with your head,

             E   D♯ G♯m
Dance, dance, dance till you're dead.

          C♯   F♯   G♯m
Off, off, off with your head,

             E   F♯ G♯m
Dance, dance, dance till you're dead.

          N.C.
Off, off, off with your head,

Dance, dance, dance till you're dead.

Off, off, off with your head,

Dance, dance, dance till you're dead.

Heavy Cross

Words & Music by
Mary Beth Patterson, Nathan Howdeshell & Hannah Billie

Em   D   Dm   D/E

Intro

‖: Em | Em | D | D :‖

(D)   **Em**   **D**
Ooh, ooh, ooh, ooh. Ooh, ooh, ooh, ooh.

               Em   **D**
Ooh, ooh, ooh, ooh. Ooh, ooh, ooh, ooh.

Verse 1

           Em
It's a cruel, cruel world to face on your own,

     D
A heavy cross to carry along.

          Em   **D**
The lights are on, but everyone's gone and it's cruel.

          Em
It's a funny way to make ends meet,

         D
When the lights are out on every street.

        Em   **D**
It feels alright, but never complete   without joy.

Chorus 1

          Em
I trust you,

                Dm
If it's already been done, un - do it.

         Em
It takes two,

            Dm
It's up to me and you to prove it,

       Em
On the rainy nights, even the coldest days,

     Dm
You're moments ago, but seconds away.

       Em   **Dm**
The principal of nature, it's true but it's a cruel world.

Link 1

Em   D Em   D
Ooh, ooh, ooh. Ooh, ooh, ooh. Ooh, ooh, ooh. Oh, oh.

Verse 2

     Em
We can play it safe or play it cool,

D
Follow the leader or make up all the rules.

    Em   D
What - ever you want, the choice is yours so choose.

Chorus 2

    Em
I trust you,

        Dm
If it's already been done, un - do it.

    Em
It takes two,

        Dm
And it's up to me and you to prove it.

  Em   Dm
I, I, I, I, I, oh, oh, oh, yeah, oh, oh.

  Em   Dm
I, I, I, I, I, oh, oh, oh, yeah, oh, yeah, oh, yeah, oh.

Link 2   ‖: Em | Em | Em | Em :‖

63

Chorus 3

Em
I trust you,

                                  Dm
It's already been done, un - do it.

        Em
It takes two,

                         Dm
It's up to me and you to prove it.

Em   D/E
I, I, I, oh, yeah.

        Em   D/E
I, I, I, I, I, oh, oh, yeah, oh, yeah, oh, yeah, oh.

Chorus 4

        Em
I trust you,

                             Dm
If it's already been done, un - do it.

        Em
It takes two,

                        Dm
And it's up to me and you, to prove it.

      Em   Dm
I, I, I, I, I, oh, oh, yeah, oh, oh.

      Em   Dm
I, I, I, oh, oh, yeah, oh, yeah, oh, yeah, oh.

        Em
I trust you.

Gossip

Human

Words by Brandon Flowers
Music by Brandon Flowers, Dave Keuning, Mark Stoermer & Ronnie Vannucci

Bb   Dm   Eb   F   Gm   Cm   F#dim

Intro | Bb | Bb | Bb | Bb ||

Verse 1
Bb   Dm   Eb   Bb
I did my best to notice when the call came down the line,
        F   Gm   Bb   F
Up to the platform of sur - render, I was brought but I was kind.
        Bb   Dm   Eb   Gm
And sometimes I get nervous when I see an open door,
        Eb   F   Bb
Close your eyes, clear your heart,   cut the cord.

Chorus 1
Bb   Dm   Eb   Bb
Are we human   or are we dancer?
F   Gm   Eb   F
My sign is vital,   my hands are cold.
        Bb   Dm   Gm
And I'm on my knees looking for the answer,
        Cm   Eb   Bb
Are we human   or are we dancer?

Link 1 | Bb | Dm | Eb | Bb |

| F | Gm | Eb | F ||

Verse 2
(F)   Bb   Dm   Eb   Bb
Pay my re - spects to grace and virtue, send my con - dolences to good.
        F   Gm
Give my re - gards to soul and romance,
        Eb   F
They always did the best they could.
        Bb   Dm   Eb   Gm
And so long to de - votion, you taught me everything I know,
        Eb   F   Bb
Wave good - bye, wish me well,   you've got to let me go.

Chorus 2

B♭   Dm   E♭   B♭
  Are we human   or are we dancer?

F   Gm E♭   F
  My sign is vital,   my hands are cold.

         B♭   Dm   Gm
And I'm on my knees looking for the answer,

         Cm   E♭   B♭
Are we human   or are we dancer?

Bridge

(Dm)   E♭   F   F♯dim   Gm
 Will your system be al - right when you dream of home to - night?

      E♭
There is no message we're receiving,

F
Let me know, is your heart still beating?

B♭   F   Gm
  Are we human or   are we dancer?

E♭   F   Dm   E♭
  My sign is vital,   my hands are cold.

         B♭   Dm   Gm
And I'm on my knees looking for the answer,

You've got to let me know.

Chorus 3

B♭   Dm   E♭   B♭
  Are we human   or are we dancer?

F   Gm E♭   F
  My sign is vital,   my hands are cold.

         B♭   Dm   Gm
And I'm on my knees looking for the answer,

         Cm   E♭   (B♭)
Are we human   or are we dancer?

Link 2

| B♭ | Dm | E♭ | B♭ | |

| F | Gm | E♭ | F | |

| B♭ | Dm | E♭ | Gm | ‖

Outro

(Gm)   E♭   Gm   F
Are we human or are we dancer?

         E♭   Cm   B♭
Are we human   or are we dancer?

I'm Throwing My Arms Around Paris

Words & Music by
Morrissey & Martin Boorer

G   Am   F   C   D   E   Dm   Fmaj⁷

Capo second fret

Intro | G Am | F Am | G Am | F Am ‖

Verse 1

     G Am   F   Am   G   Am F Am
     In the absence of your love,

     G Am   F   Am   G   Am F Am
     And in the absence of   human touch,

     G   F
     I have de - cided...

Chorus 1

     C Am   D   F   E
     I'm throwing my arms a - round, around Paris,

     Am C   E   F
     Be - cause only stone and steel accept my love.

Verse 2

     G Am   F   Am   G   Am F Am
     In the absence of your smil - ing face,

     G Am   F   Am
     I travelled all over the place

     G   F
     And I have de - cided...

Chorus 2

     C Am   D   F   E
     I'm throwing my arms a - round, around Paris,

     Am C   E   F
     Be - cause only stone and steel accept my love.

     C Am   D   F   E
     I'm throwing my arms a - round, around Paris,

     Am C   E   G
     Be - cause only stone and steel   accept my love.

Interlude

| C Dm | Am G | C Dm | Am G |

| C Dm | Am G | E | F ||

Chorus 3

C   Am   D   F
I'm throwing my arms a - round Paris,

     E   Am   C
Be - cause no - body wants my love,

     E   F
No - body wants my love.

        G   Am F
Nobody needs my love,

Am   G   Am F
Nobody wants my love.

G   Am   F   Am
Yes, you've made yourself plain,

G   Fmaj7
Yes, you've made yourself very plain.

Jackie Collins Existential Question Time

Words by Richard Edwards
Music by James Dean Bradfield, Sean Moore & Nicholas Jones

E5   G#5   C#5   F#5   B/F#   G#m/D#   F#m/C#

E/B   A/E   G#m/B   F#m/A   Am   C   E

Capo third fret

Intro

| E5 | E5 | E5 |

| E5 | G#5 | C#5 | F#5 ‖

Verse 1

      E5   G#5   C#5   F#5
To - night we beg, to - night we beg the question,

      E5   G#5   C#5   F#5
If a married man, a married man fucks a Catholic,

           B/F# G#m/D#
And his wife dies,

B/F#   G#m/D# F#m/C#   E/B   B/F# G#m/D# B/F# G#m/D# F#m/C#
With - out   know - ing,

E/B   A/E   G#m/B F#m/A A/E   G#m/B F#m/A
Does that make him unfaithful, peo - ple?

Chorus 1

E5
Oh mummy, what's a Sex Pistol?

Oh mummy, what's a Sex Pistol?

Oh mummy, what's a Sex Pistol?

Link 1

| E5 | G#5 | C#5 | F#5 ‖

Verse 2

       E5   G♯5   C♯5   F♯5
To - night we beg, to - night we beg the question,

       E5   G♯5   C♯5   F♯5
If a married man, a married man fucks a Catholic,

           B/F♯ G♯m/D♯
Does that mean you,

B/F♯ G♯m/D♯ F♯m/C♯ E/B   B/F♯ G♯m/D♯ B/F♯ G♯m/D♯ F♯m/C♯
Have gone   to   seed?

E/B   A/E   G♯m/B F♯m/A A/E   G♯m/B F♯m/A
Or does that mean you owe him no -   thing?

Chorus 2

       E5
Oh mummy, what's a Sex Pistol?

Oh mummy, what's a Sex Pistol?

Oh mummy, what's a Sex Pistol?

Outro

       Am   C   E
A situationist sisterhood of Jackie and Joan,

Am   C   E
Separates us, the question's without a home.

       Am   C   E
A situationist sisterhood of Jackie and Joan,

Am   C   E
Separates us, the question's without a home.

Jump In The Pool

Words & Music by
Paul Epworth, Edward MacFarlane, Edward Gibson & Jack Savidge

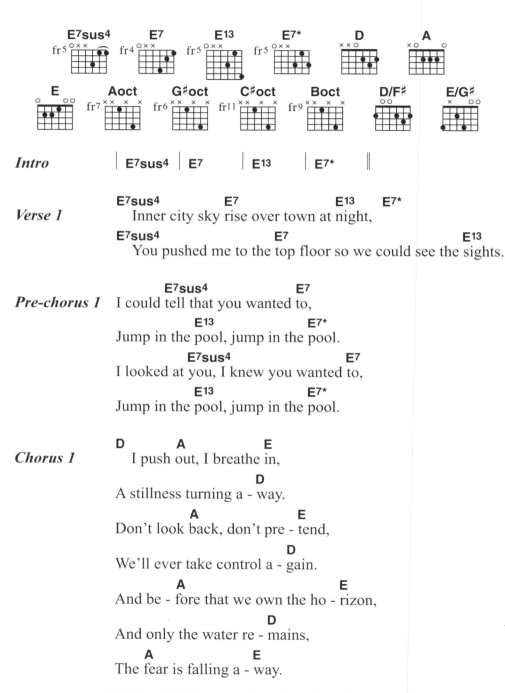

Intro | E7sus4 | E7 | E13 | E7* ‖

Verse 1
E7sus4   E7   E13   E7*
Inner city sky rise over town at night,
E7sus4   E7   E13   E7*
You pushed me to the top floor so we could see the sights.

Pre-chorus 1
           E7sus4   E7
I could tell that you wanted to,
              E13   E7*
Jump in the pool, jump in the pool.
              E7sus4   E7
I looked at you, I knew you wanted to,
              E13   E7*
Jump in the pool, jump in the pool.

Chorus 1
        D   A   E
I push out, I breathe in,
                           D
A stillness turning a - way.
                  A   E
Don't look back, don't pre - tend,
                              D
We'll ever take control a - gain.
                  A   E
And be - fore that we own the ho - rizon,
                           D
And only the water re - mains,
                  A   E
The fear is falling a - way.

Verse 2
    Aoct   **G#oct**   **C#oct** **Boct**
On the poolside star - ing into glowing blue,
    Aoct   **G#oct**   **C#oct** **Boct**
Swimsuit issues, with my toes curled in the grooves.

Pre-chorus 2
         Aoct   **G#oct**
I could tell that you wanted to,
       C#oct   **Boct**
Jump in the pool, jump in the pool.
      Aoct   **G#oct**
I looked at you, I knew you wanted to,
       C#oct   **Boct**
Jump in the pool, jump in the pool.

Chorus 2   As Chorus 1

Bridge 1
E   **D/F#**   **E/G#**   **D**
Keep breathing,   keep searching,   keep holding on.
E   **D/F#**   **E/G#**   **D**
 Keep breathing,   keep living,   keep holding on.

Link 1   ‖: **D** | **D** | **D** | **D**   :‖

Instr.   ‖: **D** | **A** | **E** | **E**   :‖ *Play 4 times*

Chorus 3   As Chorus 1

(Drums)
                  8
Outro   ‖: ⊢——————————⊣ :‖

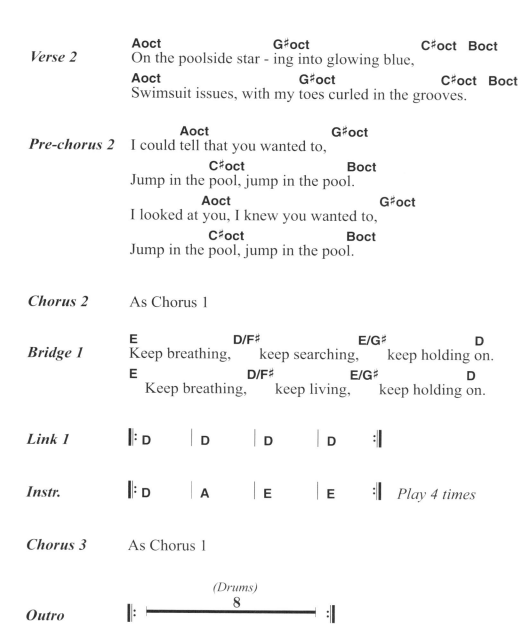

Kids

Words & Music by
Andrew Vanwyngarden & Benjamin Goldwasser

F#m   D   A   E/G#   E/A   E   Bm

Intro

| N.C. | N.C. | N.C. | N.C. |

| F#m | D | A | E/G# : | *Play 3 times*

| F#m | D | A | E/A ‖

Verse 1

F#m   D   A   E/G#
You were a child crawling on your knees toward it.

F#m   D   A   E/G#
Making mama so proud,   but your voice is too loud.

F#m D   A   E/G#
     We like to watch you laughing,

F#m   D
You pick the insects off plants,

A   E/A
No time to think of conse - quences.

Chorus 1

F#m   D   A   E/G#
Control yourself,   take only what you need from it.

F#m   D   A   E/G#
A family of trees wanted   to be haunted.

F#m   D   A   E/G#
Control yourself,   take only what you need from it.

F#m   D   A   E/A
A family of trees wanted   to be haunted.

Verse 2

F♯m   D   A   E/G♯
The water is warm, but it's sending me shivers.

F♯m   D   A   E/G♯
A baby is born   crying out for at - tention.

F♯m   D   A   E/G♯
The memories fade, like looking through a fogged mirror.

    F♯m   D
De - cision to decisions are made and not bought,

      A   E/A
But I thought this wouldn't hurt a lot, I guess not.

Chorus 2   As Chorus 1

Instr.

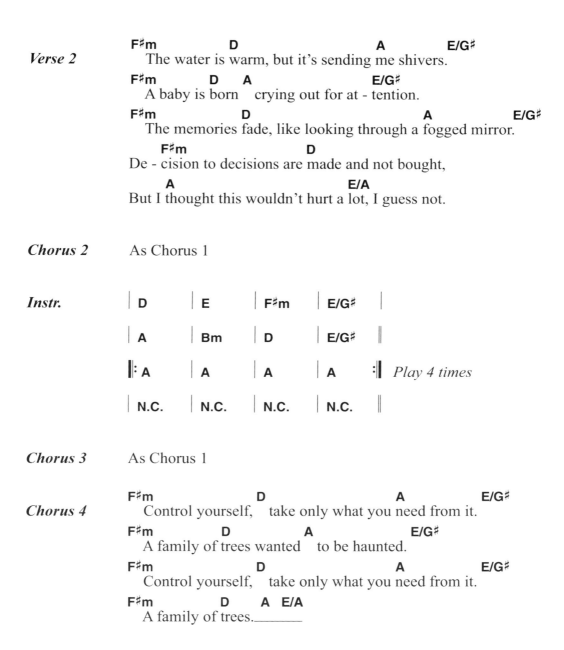

Chorus 3   As Chorus 1

Chorus 4

F♯m   D   A   E/G♯
Control yourself,   take only what you need from it.

F♯m   D   A   E/G♯
A family of trees wanted   to be haunted.

F♯m   D   A   E/G♯
Control yourself,   take only what you need from it.

F♯m   D   A   E/A
A family of trees._____

The Kids Are Sick Again

Words & Music by
Paul Smith, Thomas English,
Duncan Lloyd, Archis Tiku & Lukas Wooler

D **Bm** **G** **Em** **C** **G***

Intro ‖: D | D | D | D :‖

Verse 1
D
The comforting ache of the summer holidays,

Pointless days pining, afternoons whining.

The suburbs scream at passers by,
Bm
The scream of escape, a new siren.
G
Wasted lives, hope takes flight.

Chorus 1
G   Em
I don't mind losing self re - spect,
              Bm   C
I've done it before   and I'll do it again.
G   Em
I'm stifled tonight which is fine,
              Bm   C
I've done it before   and I'll do it again.

Link 1
| D | D | D | D |
| Bm | Bm | Bm | Bm ‖

Verse 2

D   Bm
I'm hotter than this under regular beams of   light.

Toothpaste smiles don't seem so bright.

        G
I'm marching on, don't revise.

Chorus 2

G   Em
I don't mind losing self re - spect,

                          Bm   C
I've done it before   and I'll do it again.

G   Em
I'm thwarted tonight, which is fine,

                          Bm   C
See, I've done it before   and I'll do it again.

Outro

G*   D   Em   Bm   C   G*
    The kids are sick again,   nothing to look forward to.

                      D   Em   Bm   C   G*
They jumped the cliff again,   future sinks be - neath the blue.

                    D   Em   Bm   C   G*
The kids are sick again,   nothing to look forward to.

                      D   Em   Bm   C   G*
They jumped the cliff again,   future sinks be - neath the blue.

                    D   Em   Bm   C   G*
The kids are sick again,   nothing to look forward to.

                      D   Em   Bm   C   G*
They jumped the cliff again,   future sinks be - neath the blue.

                    D   Em   Bm   C   G*
The kids are sick again,   nothing to look forward to.

| D | D | D | D   ‖

Life In Technicolor II

Words & Music by
Guy Berryman, Chris Martin,
Jon Buckland, Will Champion & Jon Hopkins

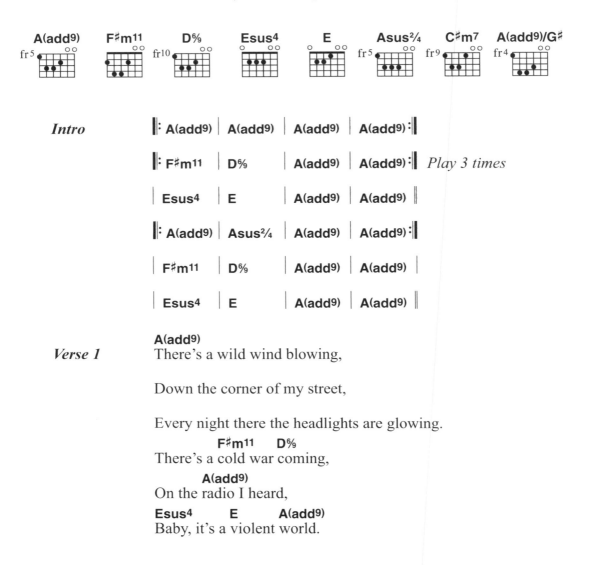

Intro

‖: A(add9) | A(add9) | A(add9) | A(add9) :‖

‖: F♯m11 | D⅚ | A(add9) | A(add9) :‖ *Play 3 times*

| Esus4 | E | A(add9) | A(add9) ‖

‖: A(add9) | Asus²⁄₄ | A(add9) | A(add9) :‖

| F♯m11 | D⅚ | A(add9) | A(add9) |

| Esus4 | E | A(add9) | A(add9) ‖

Verse 1

A(add9)
There's a wild wind blowing,

Down the corner of my street,

Every night there the headlights are glowing.
    F♯m11   D⅚
There's a cold war coming,
    A(add9)
On the radio I heard,
Esus4   E   A(add9)
Baby, it's a violent world.

Chorus 1

    F♯m11   **D⁶⁄₉** **C♯m7**
Oh, love don't let me go,

      F♯m11   **D⁶⁄₉**   **C♯m7**
Won't you take me where the streetlights glow?

     F♯m11 **D⁶⁄₉**
I can hear it coming,

      A(add9) **A(add9)/G♯** **F♯m11**
I can hear the siren's   sound,

      Esus4 **E**   **A(add9)**
Now my feet won't touch the ground.

Link 1   ‖: **F♯m11** | **D⁶⁄₉** | **A(add9)** | **A(add9)** :‖

Verse 2

F♯m11   **D⁶⁄₉**
Time came a - creeping,

    A(add9)
Oh, and time's a loaded gun,

     F♯m11 **D⁶⁄₉** **A(add9)**
Every road is a ray of light.

      F♯m11 **D⁶⁄₉**
It goes on,————

A(add9)
Time only can lead you on,

    Esus4   **E**   **A(add9)**
Still it's such a beautiful night.

Chorus 2

    F♯m11   **D⁶⁄₉** **C♯m7**
Oh, love don't let me go,

      F♯m11   **D⁶⁄₉**   **C♯m7**
Won't you take me where the streetlights glow?

     F♯m11 **D⁶⁄₉**
I can hear it coming,

      A(add9) **A(add9)/G♯** **F♯m11**
Like a sere - nade of   sound,

      Esus4 **E**   **A(add9)**
Now my feet won't touch the ground.

Chorus 3 | **F♯m11** | **D⁶⁄₉** | **C♯m7** | **C♯m7** |

     F♯m11 **D⁶⁄₉** **C♯m7**
Oh,   oh, oh.

F♯m11   **D⁶⁄₉**
Gravity re - lease me,

      A(add9) **A(add9)G♯** **F♯m11**
And don't ever hold me down,

     Esus4 **E**   **A(add9)**
Now my feet won't touch the ground.

Love Is Noise

Words & Music by
Richard Ashcroft, Nick McCabe, Simon Jones & Peter Salisbury

Em	G	D(add11)	C

Intro

Em   G
Ooh, ooh, ooh, ooh, ooh, ooh.

D(add11)   C
Ah, ha, ah, ha, ah, ha.

Em   G   D(add11)
Ooh, ooh, ooh, ooh, ooh, ooh. (Ooh, ooh, ooh, ooh, ooh.)

            C
Ah, ha, ah, ha, ah, ha. (Ah, ha, ah, ha.)

Em   G   D(add11)
Ooh, ooh, ooh, ooh, ooh, ooh. (Ooh, ooh, ooh, ooh, ooh.)

            C
Ah, ha, ah, ha, ah, ha. (Ah, ha, ah, ha.)

Em   G   D(add11)
Ooh, ooh, ooh, ooh, ooh, ooh. (Ooh, ooh, ooh, ooh, ooh.)

            C
Ah, ha, ah, ha, ah, ha

Verse 1

(C)   Em G   D(add11) C
And will those feet in modern times,

      Em   G   D(add11) C
Walk on soles that are made in China?

        Em   G   D(add11) C
Through the bright pro - saic malls,

       Em   G   D(add11) C
And the corridors that go on and on and on.

Pre-chorus 1

      Em   G
Are we blind, can't we see?

    D(add11)   C
We are one, incom - plete.

      Em   G
Are we blind in the shade?

      D(add11)   C
Waiting for life waiting to be saved, yeah.

Chorus 1

(C)   Em   G
'Cause love is noise, love is pain,

              D(add11)   C
Love is these blues that I'm singing a - gain.

          Em   G
Love is noise, love is pain,

              D(add11)   C   (Em)
Love is these blues that I'm singing a - gain, again, a - gain.

Link 1

Em   G
  Ooh, ooh, ooh, ooh, ooh, ooh.

D(add11)   C
  Ah, ha, ah, ha, ah, ha.

Em   G
  Ooh, ooh, ooh, ooh, ooh, ooh.

D(add11)   C
Ah, ha, ah, ha, ah, ha.

Verse 2

(C)   Em   G   D(add11) C
Will those feet in modern times,

         Em   G   D(add11) C
Under - stand this world's affliction?

(C)   Em   G   D(add11) C
Recog - nise the righteous anger,

         Em   G   D(add11) C
Under - stand this world's addiction?

Pre-chorus 2

      Em   G
I was blind, couldn't see,

        D(add11) C
What was here in   me.

      Em   G
I was blind, inse - cure,

        D(add11)   C
Felt like the road was way too long, yeah.

Chorus 2

(C)   Em   G
'Cause love is noise, love is pain,

              D(add11)   C
Love is these blues that I'm singing a - gain.

          Em   G
Love is noise, love is pain,

               D(add11)   C
Love is these blues that I'm singing a - gain.

cont.

      Em   **G**
Love is noise, love is pain,

        D(add11)   **C**
Love is these blues that I'm feeling a - gain.

      Em   **G**
Love is noise, love is pain,

        D(add11)   **C**   **(Em)**
Love is these blues that I'm singing a - gain, again, a - gain.

Instr.   ‖: **Em** | **G** | **D(add11)**| **C**   :‖

Bridge

Em   **G**   **D(add11)**
  Ooh, ooh, ooh, ooh, ooh, ooh. (Ooh, ooh, ooh, ooh, ooh.)

                C
Ah, ha, ah, ha, ah, ha. (Ah, ha, ah, ha.)

Em   **G**   **D(add11)**
  Ooh, ooh, ooh, ooh, ooh, ooh. (Ooh, ooh, ooh, ooh, ooh.)

                C
Ah, ha, ah, ha, ah, ha. (Ah, ha, ah, ha.)

Em   **G**   **D(add11)**
  Ooh, ooh, ooh, ooh, ooh, ooh. (Ooh, ooh, ooh, ooh, ooh.)

                C
Ah, ha, ah, ha, ah, ha. (Ah, ha, ah, ha.)

Em   **G**   **D(add11)**
  Ooh, ooh, ooh, ooh, ooh, ooh. (Ooh, ooh, ooh, ooh, ooh.)

                C
Ah, ha, ah, ha, ah, ha.

Chorus 3

(C)   **Em**   **G**
'Cause love is noise, love is pain,

        D(add11)   **C**
Love is these blues that you're feeling a - gain.

      Em   **G**
Love is noise, love is pain,

        D(add11)   **C**
Love is these blues that I'm singing a - gain.

      Em   **G**
Love is noise, love is pain,

        D(add11)   **C**
Love is these blues that I'm singing a - gain.

      Em   **G**
Love is noise, love is pain,

        D(add11)   **C**
Love is these blues that I'm singing a - gain, again...

Verse 3

(C)　　　　　**Em**　**G**
Will those feet in modern times,

D(add11
Walk on soles made in China?

　　　　　Em　**G**
Will those feet in modern times,

　　　　D(add11)　　**C**
See the bright prosaic malls?

　　　　　Em　**G**
Will those feet in modern times,

　　　　D(add11)　　　**C**
Recog - nise the heavy burden?

D(add11)　　　　　**C**
Pardon me for my sins?

Chorus 4

(C)　　　　　　**Em**　　　　**G**
'Cause love is noise, love is pain,

　　　　　D(add11)　　　　　　　　**C**
Love is these blues that you're feeling a - gain.

　　　Em　　　　**G**
Love is noise, love is pain,

　　　　　D(add11)　　　　　　　　**C**　　　　　　**(Em)**
Love is these blues that I'm singing a - gain, again, a - gain.

Outro

Em　　　　　　　　　　　**G**
　Ooh, ooh, ooh, ooh, ooh, ooh.

D(add11)　　　　　**C**
　Ah, ha, ah, ha, ah, ha.

Em　　　　　　　　　　　**G**
　Ooh, ooh, ooh, ooh, ooh, ooh.

D(add11)　　　　　**C**
　Ah, ha, ah, ha, ah, ha.　*To fade*

Love You Better

Words & Music by
Rupert Jarvis, Orlando Weeks, Felix White & Hugo White

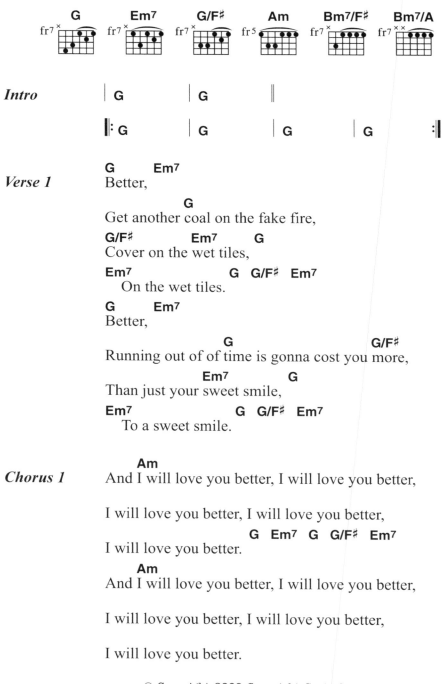

Intro | G | G ||

||: G | G | G | G :||

Verse 1

G   Em⁷
Better,

      G
Get another coal on the fake fire,

G/F♯   Em⁷   G
Cover on the wet tiles,

Em⁷   G G/F♯ Em⁷
  On the wet tiles.

G   Em⁷
Better,

               G   G/F♯
Running out of of time is gonna cost you more,

         Em⁷   G
Than just your sweet smile,

Em⁷   G G/F♯ Em⁷
  To a sweet smile.

Chorus 1

      Am
And I will love you better, I will love you better,

I will love you better, I will love you better,
               G Em⁷ G G/F♯ Em⁷
I will love you better.

      Am
And I will love you better, I will love you better,

I will love you better, I will love you better,

I will love you better.

Link 1 | G | G | G | G   ‖

Verse 2
G   **Em⁷**
Headway,

          G
Learn to love a thriller,

              G/F♯   **Em⁷**   **G**
So the words you leave me on my pillow read better,

Em⁷   **G**   **G/F♯** **Em⁷**
  Cheap card for - ever.

G   **Em⁷**
Headway,

          G
Can pull it a - part and in time,

   G/F♯   **Em⁷**   **G**
You see it's going better than ev - er,

Em⁷   **G**
  It's going better than ev - er,

        G/F♯   **Em⁷**
Harder for safe guard in your bed clothes.

Chorus 2
Am
I will love you better, I will love you better,

I will love you better, I will love you better,
               G **Em⁷** **G** **G/F♯** **Em⁷**
I will love you better.

     Am
And I will love you better, I will love you better,

I will love you better, I will love you better,

I will love you better.

Interlude 1 | G | G | G | G |
                | Bm⁷/F♯ | Bm⁷/F♯ | Bm⁷/F♯ | Bm⁷/F♯   ‖

85

                                         G
Bridge   And the thought and the thought and the thought of you,
                                                                    Bm7/A
                      I thought we'd be doing the fateful few to - gether, together.
                                         G
                      And I'd thought that you might feel the same,

                      With your insect skin and my lion's mane,
                           Bm7/A
                      And be you, tu be you.
                                  G
                      And the thought of you was crystal clear,

                      I could warn myself or bin you dear,
                           Bm7/A
                      And been you, and been you.

Interlude 2 | **G** | **G** | **G** | **G** |

                | **Bm7/A** | **Bm7/A** | **Bm7/A** | **Bm7/A**   ‖
                        (G)
                      To be you.

Outro   ‖: **G** | **Em7** | **G** | **G/F♯** **Em7** :‖ **G**   ‖

86

Magnificent

Words by Bono & The Edge
Music by U2, Brian Eno & Daniel Lanois

Chord diagrams: F♯, F♯m, C♯m (fr4), A (fr9), E (fr12), B (fr7), Bm (fr7), D (fr10)

Intro   ‖: F♯ | F♯ | F♯ | F♯ :‖

| F♯ | F♯ | F♯m | C♯m | A | E ‖

      B
Mag - nificent.

| F♯m | C♯m | A ‖

E   **B**   **Bm**
Oh, oh, mag - nificent.

Verse 1

F♯m   **C♯m A**   **E**   **B**   **Bm**
  I was born, I was born to be with you,
             F♯m
In this space and time.

      C♯m A   **E**   **B**   **Bm**
After that   and ever after I haven't had a clue,
            F♯m
Only to break rhyme.

        C♯m A   **E**   **B**   **Bm**
This foolish - ness   can leave a heart black and blue.

Oh, oh.

Chorus 1

F♯m   **C♯m A**   **E**   **B**   **Bm**
  Only love,   only love can leave such a mark.
F♯m   **C♯m A**   **E**   **B**   **Bm**
  But only love,   only love can heal such a scar.

Verse 2

F♯m   C♯m A   E   B   Bm
I was born,   I was born to sing for you.

       F♯m   C♯m
I didn't have a choice but to lift you up,

A   E   B   Bm
And sing what - ever song you wanted me to.

                F♯m
I give you back my voice,

         C♯m A   E   B   Bm
From the womb   my first cry, it was a joyful noise.

Oh, oh.

Chorus 2   As Chorus 1

Bridge

F♯m   C♯m   A   E
Justi - fied till we die, you and I will magnify, oh, oh,

       B   D   A   C♯m   (F♯)
The mag - nificent,   mag - nificent, oh,___ ooh.

Interlude ‖: F♯ | F♯ | F♯ | F♯ :‖

Instr.   ‖: F♯ | C♯m | A | E | B | Bm :‖

Chorus 3

F♯m   C♯m A   E   B   Bm
Only love,   only love can leave such a mark.

F♯m   C♯m A   E   B   Bm
But only love,   only love unites our hearts.

Outro

F♯m   C♯m   A   E
Justi - fy till we die, you and I will magnify, oh, oh,

       B   Bm   B   Bm   B   Bm F♯m
The mag - nificent,   mag - nificent,   mag - nificent.

Many Shades Of Black

Words & Music by
Jack White & Brendan Benson

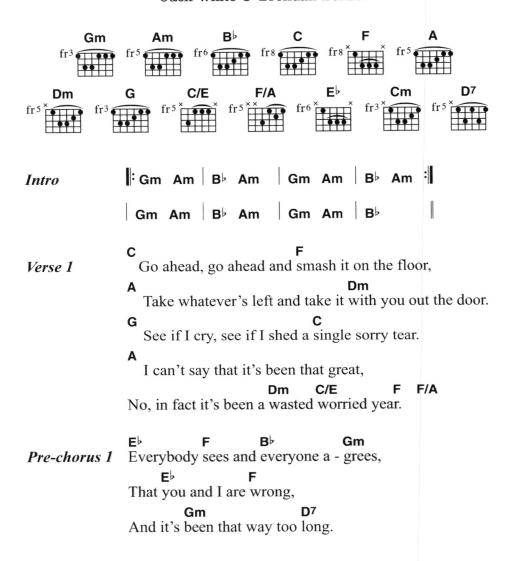

Intro   ‖: Gm Am | B♭ Am | Gm Am | B♭ Am :‖

| Gm Am | B♭ Am | Gm Am | B♭   ‖

Verse 1

C   F
Go ahead, go ahead and smash it on the floor,

A   Dm
Take whatever's left and take it with you out the door.

G   C
See if I cry, see if I shed a single sorry tear.

A
I can't say that it's been that great,

              Dm   C/E   F   F/A
No, in fact it's been a wasted worried year.

Pre-chorus 1

E♭   F   B♭   Gm
Everybody sees and everyone a - grees,

        E♭   F
That you and I are wrong,

        Gm   D⁷
And it's been that way too long.

Chorus 1

    Eb   F   Bb   Gm
Take it as it comes and be thankful when it's done.
           Eb   F
There's so many ways to act,
         Gm   Bb
And there's many shades of black,
         Gm   Bb
There's so many shades of black,
         Gm   Bb
There's so many shades of black.

Verse 2

    C   F
  Let it out, let it all out and say what's on your mind.
         A
You can kick and scream and shout,
              Dm
And say things   that are so unkind.
       G   C
Yeah, see if I care, see if I stand firm or if I fall.
            A
'Cause in the back of my mind and on the tip of my tongue,
         Dm   C/E F   F/A
Is the answer to it all.

Pre-chorus 2   As Pre-chorus 1

Chorus 2

    Eb   F   Bb   Gm
Take it as it comes and be thankful when it's done.
           Eb   F
There's so many ways to act,
         Gm   Bb
And there's many shades of black,
         Gm   Bb
Oh, there's many shades of black,
          Gm   Bb   C
Yeah, there's many shades of black. Oh.

Guitar solo

‖: Dm | Gm | Dm | Gm :‖

| C | F | C | F |

| A | Dm | A | Dm ‖

Pre-chorus 3

    (Dm) E♭   F   B♭
Yeah, everybody sees and everyone a - grees,

     E♭   F
That you and I are wrong,

     Gm   D7
And it's been that way too long.

Chorus 3

    E♭   F   B♭   Gm
Baby take it as it comes and be thankful when it's done.

     E♭   F
There's so many ways to act,

    Gm   B♭
And you cannot take it back,

    Gm   B♭
Oh, you cannot take it back,

     Gm   B♭
'Cause there's many shades of black.

    Gm   B♭
You have many shades of black,

    Gm   B♭
You have many, you have many, ooh,

    Gm   B♭
You have many shades of black.

    Gm   B♭
Oh, and many shades of black.

     Gm   B♭
There's so many shades of black,

     Gm   B♭
There's so many shades of black,

     Gm   B♭
There's so many shades of black.

    Gm   B♭   C
Oh, oh, oh, oh.

Mountains

Words & Music by
Simon Neil

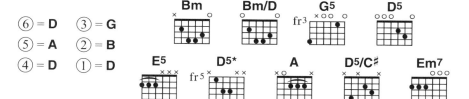

⑥ = D   ③ = G
⑤ = A   ② = B
④ = D   ① = D

Intro ∣ Bm Bm/D ∣ Bm Bm/D ‖

Verse 1

Bm   Bm/D G5
   I took a bite out of a mountain range,

                                                         D5 Bm
Thought my teeth would break, the mountain did.

                            Bm/D G5
Let's go, I want to go,

All the way to the horizon.

Verse 2

Bm   E5 G5
   I took a drink out of the ocean and,

                                 D5* Bm
I'm treading water there before I drown.

                          E5 G5
Let's dive, I want to dive,

                        D5* A
To the bottom of the ocean.

Pre-chorus 1

           A
Took a ride, I took a ride,
                 Bm   D5* A
I wouldn't go there without you.

Let's take a ride, we'll take a ride,
                 Bm   D5/C♯
I wouldn't leave here without you.

Chorus 1

D5   D5/C♯ D5   D5/C♯
I am a mountain,   I am the sea,
Bm   D5/C♯
You can't take that away from me.
D5   D5/C♯ D5   D5/C♯
I am a mountain,   I am the sea,
Bm
You can't take that away from me.

Bridge 1

         A   Bm   G5
'Cause you tear us apart,
                 D5   A
With all the things you don't like.
    Bm   G5
You can't under - stand,
    D5   A
That I won't leave,
    Bm   G5
Till we're finished here.
    D5   A
And then you'll find out,
      Bm   G5   D5
Where it all went wrong.

Verse 3

Bm   E5 G5
I wrote a note to the jungle and,
                                                  D5* Bm
They wrote me back that I was never crowned,
                     E5 G5
King of the jungle so,
                               D5* A
There's an end to my horizon.

Pre-chorus 2   As Pre-chorus 1

Chorus 2

D5   **D5/C♯**   **D5**   **D5/C♯**
I am a mountain,   I am the sea,

Bm   **D5/C♯**
You can't take that away from me.

D5   **D5/C♯**   **D5**   **D5/C♯**
I am a mountain,   I am the sea.

Bridge 2   As Bridge 1

Instr. | **Bm** **A** | **D5** | **Bm** **A** | **G5** |

           | **Bm** **A** | **D5** | **E5** | **G5** ||

Middle

Bm   **A**   **D5**   **G5**   **D5**
Nothing lasts for - ever, ex - cept you and me,

A   **D5**   **G5**   **Em7**
You are my mountain,   you are my sea.

Bm   **A**   **D5**   **G5**   **D5**
Love can last for - ever   be - tween you and me,

A   **D5**   **G5**   **D5/C♯**
You are my mountain,   you are my sea.

Chorus 3

D5   **D5/C♯**   **D5**   **D5/C♯**
I am a mountain,   I am the sea,

Bm
You can't take that away from me.

D5
I am a mountain, I am the sea,

                          N.C.
I am a mountain,   I am the sea.

95

My Girls

Words & Music by
David Portner, Noah Lennox & Brian Weitz

C	F	Fmaj7	G6

Fade in

Intro   ‖: C | C | C | C :‖

Verse 1

C

There isn't much that I feel I need,

A solid soul and the blood I bleed.

But with a little girl and by my spouse,

I only want a proper house.

There isn't much that I feel I need,

A solid soul and the blood I bleed.

With a little girl and by my spouse,

I only want a proper house.

Link 1   ‖: C | C | C | C :‖

Verse 2   As Verse 1

Chorus 1

F   C
I don't care for fancy things,

  F   C
Or to take part in the freshest wave.

   F   C
But to provide for mine who ask,

  F   C
I will with heart over my father's grave.

F   C
I don't care for fancy things,

  F   C
Or to take part in the freshest wave.

   F   C
But to provide for mine who ask,

  F   C
I will with heart over my father's grave.

Over my father's grave.

Over my father's grave.

Over my father's grave.

Over my father's grave.

Over my father's grave.

Over my father's grave.

Over my father's grave.

Over my father's grave.

Bridge 1

C   G6   Fmaj7
 I don't mean to seem like I care,

     G6
About material things like a social status.

C   G6   Fmaj7   G6
 I just want four walls and a - dobe slats for my girls.

C   G6   Fmaj7
 I don't mean to seem like I care,

     G6
About material things like a social status.

C   Fmaj7   G6
 I just want four walls and a - dobe slats for my girls.

Verse 3

               C
There isn't much that I feel I need,

A solid soul and the blood I bleed.

With a little girl and by my spouse,

I only want a proper house.

Chorus 2

     F   **C**
I don't care for fancy things,
       F   **C**
Or to take part in the freshest wave.
       F   **C**
But to provide for mine who ask,
      F   **C**
I will with heart over my father's grave.

Over my father's grave.

Over my father's grave.

Over my father's grave.

Over my father's grave.

Over my father's grave.

Over my father's grave.

Over my father's grave.

Over my father's grave.

Bridge 2   As Bridge 1

Bridge 3   As Bridge 1

Outro   ‖: C | C | C | C   :‖   *Repeat to fade*

My Mistakes Were Made For You

Words & Music by
Alex Turner & Miles Kane

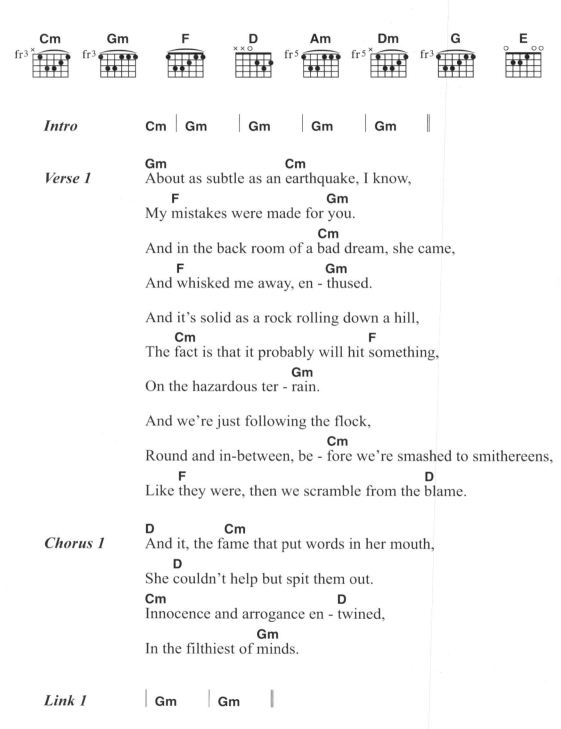

Intro

| Cm | Gm | Gm | Gm | Gm ‖

Verse 1

Gm   Cm
About as subtle as an earthquake, I know,

  F   Gm
My mistakes were made for you.

       Cm
And in the back room of a bad dream, she came,

  F   Gm
And whisked me away, en - thused.

And it's solid as a rock rolling down a hill,

  Cm   F
The fact is that it probably will hit something,

    Gm
On the hazardous ter - rain.

And we're just following the flock,

       Cm
Round and in-between, be - fore we're smashed to smithereens,

  F   D
Like they were, then we scramble from the blame.

Chorus 1

  D   Cm
And it, the fame that put words in her mouth,

  D
She couldn't help but spit them out.

Cm   D
Innocence and arrogance en - twined,

      Gm
In the filthiest of minds.

Link 1

| Gm | Gm ‖

Verse 2

       Gm   **Cm**
She was bitten on her birthday and now,

    F   **Gm**
A face in the crowd, she's not.

                              Cm
And I suspect that now, for - ever the shape,

    F   **D**
She came to escape is for - got.

Chorus 2

    D   **Cm**
And it's a lot to ask her not to sting,

      D
And give her less than everything,

      Cm   **D**
A - round your crooked conscience she will wind.

Link 2 | **Gm** | **Gm**   ‖

Instr. | **Am** | **Dm** | **G** | **Am**   ‖

Verse 3

Am
'Cause we're just following the flock,

                         Dm
Round the in-between, be - fore we're smashed to smithereens,

      G   **E**
Like they were, then we scramble from the blame.

Chorus 3

    E   **Dm**
And it, the fame that put words in her mouth,

      E
She couldn't help but spit them out.

      Dm   **E**
A - round your crooked conscience she will wind.

            Dm
And it's a lot to ask her not to sting,

      E
And give her less than everything,

Dm   **E**
Innocence and arrogance en - twined.

Outro   ‖: **A** | **Am** | **Am** | **Am**   :‖   *Play 4 times*

           | **Am**   ‖

Mykonos

Words & Music by
Robin Pecknold

C#m/G#   B/F#   A/E   G#m/D#   A

C#m   B6   A6   G#m   F#m

Intro

‖: C#m/G# B/F# A/E G#m/D# | A/E A B/F# G#m/D# :‖

C#m B6 A6 G#m A6 G#m C#m
Oh._____

　　　 B6 A6 G#m A6 G#m C#m
Oh._____

Verse 1

C#m　　　　　　 B6　　　A6　　 B6　　G#m　　A6
The door slammed loud and rose up a cloud of dust on us.

C#m　　 B6　　A6　　　　　　　 B6　　G#m　　　A6
Footsteps follow down through the hollow sound, torn up.

Chorus 1

　　　　 F#m　　　　　　　 C#m
And you will go to Myko - nos,

　　　　 G#m　　　　　　 C#m
With a vision of the gentle coast,

　　　　 F#m　　　　　　　 C#m
And a sun to maybe dissi - pate,

　　　　 G#m　　　　　　 A6　 B6
Shadows of the mess you made.

Link 1

C#m B6 A6 G#m A6 G#m C#m
Oh._____

　　　 B6 A6 G#m A6 G#m C#m
Oh._____

Verse 2

C#m　　　 B6　A6　　　　　 B6　　　　 G#m　　A6
How did any moles in the snow tipped pines, I find,

C#m　　 B6　　　A6　　 B6　　　 G#m　　 A6
Hatching from the seed of your thin mind, all night?

Chorus 2	As Chorus 1

Link 2	As Link 1

Interlude

            C♯m/G♯ B/F♯ A/E G♯m/D♯ B6
Ooh,___ Oh._____

            C♯m/G♯ B/F♯ A/E G♯m/D♯ A6
Ooh,___ Oh._____

            C♯m/G♯ B/F♯ A/E G♯m/D♯ B6
Ooh,___ Oh._____

N.C.
Ooh.___

Bridge 1

N.C. (C♯m)   (B6)   (A6)
Brother you don't need to turn me a - way,

(C♯m)   (B6)   (A6)
I was waiting down at the ancient gates.

F♯m   B6
   You go wher - ever you go today,

F♯m   B6
   You go to - day.

C♯m   B6   A6
   I remember how they took you down,

C♯m   B6   A6
   As the winter turned the meadow a - round.

F♯m   B6
   You go wher - ever you go today,

F♯m   B6
   You go to - day.

C♯m   B6   A6
   When I'm walking brother don't you for - get,

C♯m   B6   A6
   It ain't often that you'd ever find a friend,

F♯m   B6
   You go wher - ever you go today,

F♯m   B6
   You go to - day.

Outro

|: F♯m   B6
    You go wher - ever you go today,

F♯m   B6
   You go to - day. :| *Repeat to fade*

Never Miss A Beat

Words & Music by
Charlie Wilson, Nicholas Hodgson,
Andrew White, James Rix & Nicholas Baines

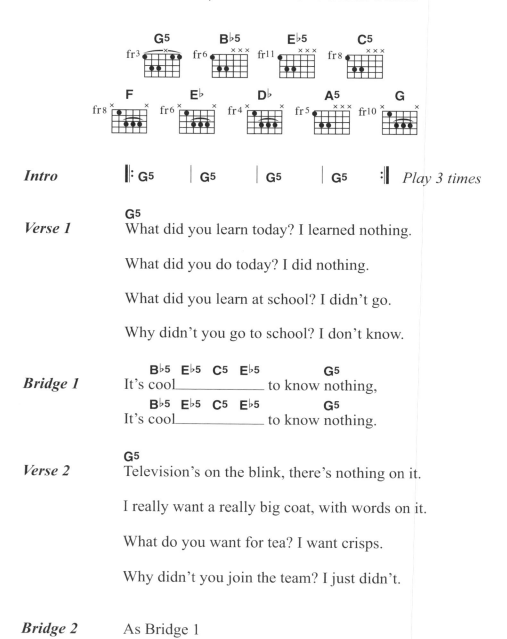

Intro ‖: G5 | G5 | G5 | G5 :‖ *Play 3 times*

Verse 1

G5
What did you learn today? I learned nothing.

What did you do today? I did nothing.

What did you learn at school? I didn't go.

Why didn't you go to school? I don't know.

Bridge 1

B♭5 E♭5 C5 E♭5   G5
It's cool_____ to know nothing,

B♭5 E♭5 C5 E♭5   G5
It's cool_____ to know nothing.

Verse 2

G5
Television's on the blink, there's nothing on it.

I really want a really big coat, with words on it.

What do you want for tea? I want crisps.

Why didn't you join the team? I just didn't.

Bridge 2   As Bridge 1

Chorus 1

G⁵
Take a look, take a look, take a look at the kids on the street, **F**

No, they never miss a beat, no, they never miss a beat, **D♭**

E♭   **F**
Never miss a beat, never miss a beat, beat, beat, beat.

D♭
Take a look at the kids on the street,

E♭   **F**
No, they never miss a beat, no, they never miss a beat,

Never miss a beat, never miss a, never miss a beat, never miss a beat.

Link 1   ‖: G⁵ | G⁵ | G⁵ | G⁵   :‖

Verse 3

G⁵
Here comes the referee, the light's flashing.

Best bit of the day, now that's living.

Why don't you run away? Are you kidding?

What is the golden rule? You say nothing.

Bridge 3   As Bridge 1

Chorus 2   As Chorus 1

Link 2   ‖: G⁵ | G⁵ | G⁵ | G⁵   :‖

| B♭⁵ C⁵ | B♭⁵ A⁵ | G | G | G   ‖

Chorus 3

G⁵
Take a look, take a look, take a look at the kids on the street, **F**

D♭
No, they never miss a beat, no, they never miss a beat,

E♭   **F**
Never miss a beat, never miss a beat, beat, beat, beat.

D♭
Take a look at the kids on the street,

E♭   **F**
No, they never miss a beat, no, they never miss a beat,

Never miss a beat, never miss a, never miss a beat, never miss a beat.

New Divide

Words & Music by
Chester Bennington, Mike Shinoda,
Rob Bourdon, Joseph Hahn, Brad Delson & Dave Farrell

F5   A♭5   E♭5   B♭5   C5   D♭5

⑥ = D   ③ = G
⑤ = A   ② = B
④ = D   ① = E

Intro

‖: F5 | F5 | F5 | F5 :‖

‖: F5 | A♭5 | E♭5 | B♭5 C5 :‖

Verse 1

F5   A♭5   E♭5   B♭5
I re - membered black skies, the lightning all a - round me,
F5   A♭5   E♭5 B♭5
I re - membered each flash as time began to blur.
F5   A♭5   E♭5   B♭5
Like a startling sign that fate had finally found me,
D♭5   B♭5
And your voice was all I heard that I get what I deserve.

Chorus 1

(B♭5)   F5   E♭5   B♭5
So give me reason to prove me wrong, to wash this memory clean,
F5   A♭5   E♭5
Let the floods cross the distance in your eyes.
F5   A♭5   E♭5   B♭5
Give me reason to fill this hole, con - nect the space be - tween,
D♭5   E♭5   (F5)
Let it be enough to reach the truth that lies across this new di - vide

Link 1

| F5 | A♭5 | E♭5 | B♭5 C5 ‖

Verse 2

(C5)   F5   A♭5   E♭5   B♭5

There was nothing in sight but memories left a - bandoned,

F5   A♭5   E♭5 B♭5

There was nowhere to hide, the ashes fell like snow.

F5   A♭5   E♭5   B♭5

And the ground caved in be - tween where we were standing,

D♭5   B♭5

And your voice was all I heard that I get what I deserve.

Chorus 2

(B♭5)   F5   E♭5   B♭5

So give me reason to prove me wrong, to wash this memory clean,

F5   A♭5   E♭5   (F5)

Let the floods cross the distance in your eyes across this new di - vide.

Interlude

‖: F5 | F5 | F5 | F5 :‖

Bridge

N.C.   F5   A♭5   E♭5   B♭5

In every loss, in every lie, in every truth that you'd de - ny,

C5   F5   A♭5

And each re - gret and each good - bye,

E♭5   B♭5

Was a mi - stake too great to hide.

C5   D♭5   B♭5

And your voice was all I heard that I get what I deserve.

Chorus 3

C5   F5   E♭5   B♭5

So give me reason to prove me wrong, to wash this memory clean,

F5   A♭5   E♭5

Let the floods cross the distance in your eyes.

F5   A♭5   E♭5   B♭5

Give me reason to fill this hole, con - nect the space be - tween,

D♭5   E♭5   F5

Let it be enough to reach the truth that lies across this new di - vide.

A♭5 E♭5   B♭5   C5 F5

A - cross this new di - vide.

A♭5 E♭5   B♭5   C5 F5

A - cross this new di - vide.

Outro

| F5 | A♭5 | E♭5 | C5 |

| F5 | A♭5 | E♭5 | F5 ‖

No You Girls

Words & Music by
Alexander Kapranos, Nicholas McCarthy, Robert Hardy & Paul Thomson

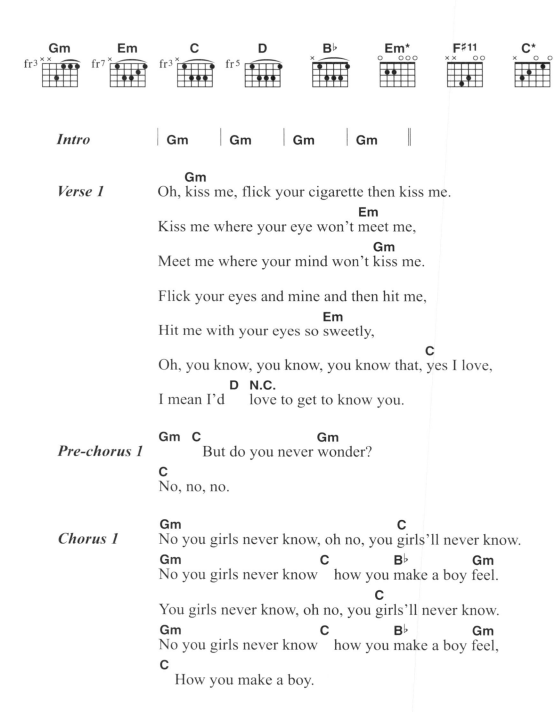

Intro | Gm | Gm | Gm | Gm ‖

Verse 1

Gm
Oh, kiss me, flick your cigarette then kiss me.
Em
Kiss me where your eye won't meet me,
Gm
Meet me where your mind won't kiss me.

Flick your eyes and mine and then hit me,
Em
Hit me with your eyes so sweetly,
C
Oh, you know, you know, you know that, yes I love,
D N.C.
I mean I'd   love to get to know you.

Pre-chorus 1

Gm C   **Gm**
        But do you never wonder?
C
No, no, no.

Chorus 1

Gm   **C**
No you girls never know, oh no, you girls'll never know.
Gm   **C**   **B♭**   **Gm**
No you girls never know   how you make a boy feel.

C
You girls never know, oh no, you girls'll never know.
Gm   **C**   **B♭**   **Gm**
No you girls never know   how you make a boy feel,
C
     How you make a boy.

| *Link 1* | | Gm | Gm | Gm | Gm | ‖

Gm

Verse 2 Oh, kiss me, flick your cigarette and then kiss me.

Em

Kiss me where your eye won't meet me,

Gm

Meet me where your eye won't flick me.

Flick your mind and mine so briefly,

Em

Oh you know, you know you're so sweetly,

C

Oh you know, you know I know that I   love you,

D   N.C.

I mean I,   I mean I need to love.

Pre-chorus 2 As Pre-chorus 1

Gm   **C**

Chorus 2 No you girls never know, oh no, you girls'll never know.

Gm   **C**   **B♭**   **Gm**

No you girls never know   how you make a boy feel.

C

You girls never know, oh no, you girls'll never know.

Gm   **C**   **B♭**   **Gm**

No you girls never know   how you make a boy feel,

C   **B♭**   **Gm C**   **B♭**

 How you make a boy feel,   how you make a boy.

Bridge

Em*   F♯11

 Sometimes I say stupid things that I think, well, I mean I,

C*   Gm   C

 Sometimes I think the stupidest things.

         Gm C   Gm C

Because I never wonder oh, how the girl feels,

        Gm

Oh, how the girl feels.

Chorus 3

Gm   C

No you boys never care, oh no, you boys'll never care,

Gm   C B♭   Gm

No you boys never care how the girl feels.

                C

You boys never care, you dirty boys'll never care,

Gm   C B♭   Gm

No you boys never care how the girl feels,

C   B♭   Gm

 Oh, how the girl feels,

C   B♭   Gm

 Oh, how the girl feels.——

Franz Ferdinand

Oxford Comma

Words & Music by
Ezra Koenig, Rostam Batmanglij,
Christopher Baio & Christopher Tomson

Chords: G, D/C, G/B, C/E, C, D, Am

Intro | G | G | G | G ||

Verse 1
G
Who gives a fuck about an Oxford comma?
D/C   G/B   C/E   C
   I've seen those English dramas too, they're cruel.
G   D/C
So if there's any other way   to spell the word,
                           G/B   C/E   C
It's fine with me, with me.

Chorus 1
C   D
Why would you speak to me that way,
      G   Am
E - specially when I always said that I,
C   D
   Haven't got the words for you?
G   Am
   All your diction   dripping with disdain,
C   D   G
   Through the pain I always tell the truth.

Verse 2
G
Who gives a fuck about an Oxford comma?
D/C   G/B C/E   C
   I climbed to Dharamsala too, I did.
G
   I met the highest Lama,
D/C   G/B   C/E   C
   His accent sounded fine to me, to me.

Chorus 2
C   D
Check your handbook,   it's no trick.
G   Am
   Take the Chapstick,   put it on your lips.

cont.

   C   D
   Crack a smile, ad - just my tie.

   G   Am
   Know your boyfriend, unlike other guys.

Bridge 1

   C   D
   Why would you lie about how much coal you have?

   G   Am
   Why would you lie about something dumb like that?

   C   D
   Why would you lie about anything at all?

   G   Am
   First the window, then it's to the wall,

   C   D   G
   Lil' Jon, he always tells the truth.

Guitar solo ‖: G | D/C | G/B | C/E C :‖ *Play 4 times*

Chorus 3

   C   D
   Check your passport, it's no trick.

   G   Am
   Take the Chapstick, put it on your lips.

   C   D
   Crack a smile, ad - just my tie.

   G   Am
   Know your butler, unlike other guys.

Bridge 2

   C   D
   Why would you lie about how much coal you have?

   G   Am
   Why would you lie about something dumb like that?

   C   D
   Why would you lie about anything at all?

   G   Am
   First the window, then it's through the wall.

   C   D
   Why would you tape my conversations?

   G   Am
   Show your paintings at the United Nations,

   C   D   (G)
   Lil' Jon, he always tells the truth.

Outro | G | G | G | G ‖

Paper Planes

Words & Music by
Mick Jones, Joe Strummer, Paul Simonon,
Topper Headon, Thomas Pentz & Mathangi Arulpragasam

Intro
| D | D   A |

| G | G |

Verse 1

‖: I fly like paper, get high like planes,
$\quad$ **D**

If you catch me at the border I got visas in my name.
$\qquad\qquad\qquad\qquad\qquad\qquad$ **A**

If you come around here, I make 'em all day,
$\quad$ **G**

I get one down in a second if you wait. :‖

‖: Sometimes I feel sitting on trains,
$\quad$ **D**

Every stop I get to I'm clocking that game.
$\qquad\qquad\qquad\qquad$ **A**

Everyone's a winner now we're making our fame,
G

Bona fide hustler making my name. :‖

Chorus 1

‖: All I wanna do is (BANG! BANG! BANG! BANG!)
$\quad$ **D**

And… (KER-CHING!)

And take your mon - ey.
$\qquad\qquad\quad$ **A**

All I wanna do is (BANG! BANG! BANG! BANG!)
G

And… (KER-CHING!)

And take your mon - ey. :‖
$\qquad\qquad\quad$ **A**

Verse 2

D
‖: Pirate skulls and bones,

A
Sticks and stones and weed and bombs.

G
Running when we hit 'em,

Lethal poison for their system. :‖

D
‖: No-one on the corner has swag like us,

A
Hit me on my banner prepaid wire - less.

G
We pack and deliver like UPS trucks,

Already going hell, just pumping that gas. :‖

Chorus 2   As Chorus 1

D
Verse 3   M.I.A., third world democracy,

A   G
Yeah, I got more records than the K.G.B.

So, uh, no funny business,

Are you all ready?

D
Some, some, some, a-some I murder,

A
Some, a-some I let go.

G
Some, some, some, a-some I murder,

Some, a-some I let go.

Chorus 3   As Chorus 1

Outro | D | D   A |

             | G | G   ‖

115

Paris Is Burning

Words & Music by
Phillipa Brown, Anuroop Pillai & Roy Kerr

Fmaj⁷ **C** **A⁷sus⁴** **D** **Esus⁴**

C⁵ **D⁵** **A⁵** **F⁵** **G⁵**

riff 1_____

Intro

G	F♯	D	C	C	D	A	A	F♯	G	A
5fr	4fr	0fr	3fr	3fr	0fr	0fr	0fr	2fr	3fr	0fr
④	④	④	⑤	⑤	④	⑤	⑤	⑥	⑥	⑤

riff 2_____

G	F♯	D	C	C	D	A	A	B	C	D
5fr	4fr	0fr	3fr	3fr	0fr	0fr	0fr	2fr	3fr	0fr
④	④	④	⑤	⑤	④	⑤	⑤	⑤	⑤	④

Verse 1

N.C. (riff 1)
All of the boys and the girls here in Paris,

riff 2
Sing to the night without sight, but with madness.

riff 1
I can't keep up, I'm a wreck but I want it,

riff 2
Tell me the truth, is it love or just Paris?

riff 1
All of the boys and the girls here in Paris,

riff 2
Sing to the night without sight, but with madness.

riff 1
I can't keep up, I'm a wreck but I want it,

riff 2
Tell me the truth, is it love or just Paris?

Chorus 1

   Fmaj⁷   **C**   **A⁷sus⁴**
My heart is yearning, but Paris is burning,

Paris is burning all night long.

Fmaj⁷   **C**   **D**
My heart is dreaming, but Paris is screaming,

   Esus⁴   **Fmaj⁷**
Paris is screaming all night long.

cont.

                   C   **A⁷sus⁴**
My heart is yearning, but Paris is burning,

Paris is burning all night long.

Fmaj⁷   **C**   **D**
 My heart is dreaming, but Paris is screaming,

         Esus⁴   **N.C. (riff 1)**
Paris is screaming all night long.

Verse 2

N.C. (riff 1)
Kids in the street drinking wine on the sidewalk,

riff 2
Saving the plans that we made till its night time.

riff 1
Give me your glass, it's your last, you're too wasted,

riff 2
Or get me one too 'cause I'm new, and need tasting.

riff 1
Kids in the street drinking wine on the sidewalk,

riff 2
Saving the plans that we made till its night time.

riff 1
Give me your glass, it's your last, you're too wasted,

riff 2
Get me one too 'cause I'm new, and need tasting.

Chorus 2

Fmaj⁷   **C**   **A⁷sus⁴**
 My heart is yearning, but Paris is burning,

Paris is burning all night long.

Fmaj⁷   **C**   **D**
 My heart is dreaming, but Paris is screaming,

         Esus⁴   **Fmaj⁷**
Paris is screaming all night long.

                   C   **A⁷sus⁴**
My heart is yearning, but Paris is burning,

Paris is burning all night long.

Fmaj⁷   **C**   **D**
 My heart is dreaming, but Paris is screaming,

         N.C. (E)
Paris is screaming all night long.

Bridge 1

C^5 D^5 A^5
I've lost my way, it's hard to find it through,

I see the night, but I lost all sight of you.

F^5 G^5 D^5
I've lost my way, it's hard to find it through,

I see the night, but I lost all sight of you.

Instr.

| Fmaj⁷ | C | A⁷sus⁴ | A⁷sus⁴ |

| Fmaj⁷ | C | D | Esus⁴ ‖

Chorus 3

Fmaj⁷   C   A⁷sus⁴
My heart is yearning, but Paris is burning,

Paris is burning all night long.

Fmaj⁷   C   D
My heart is dreaming, but Paris is screaming,

     Esus⁴   Fmaj⁷
Paris is screaming all night long.

           C   A⁷sus⁴
My heart is yearning, but Paris is burning,

Paris is burning all night long.

Fmaj⁷   C   D
My heart is dreaming, but Paris is screaming,

     Esus⁴   Fmaj⁷
Paris is screaming all night long.

Outro

Fmaj⁷   C   A⁷sus⁴
I've lost my way, it's hard to find it through,

I see the night, but I lost all sight of you.

Fmaj⁷   C   D
I've lost my way, it's hard to find it through,

     Esus⁴
I see the night, but I lost all sight of you.

Fmaj⁷   C   A⁷sus⁴
I've lost my way, it's hard to find it through,

I see the night, but I lost all sight of you.

Fmaj⁷   C   D
I've lost my way, it's hard to find it through,

     Esus⁴
I see the night, but I lost all sight of you.

Rock N Roll Train

Words & Music by
Angus Young & Malcolm Young

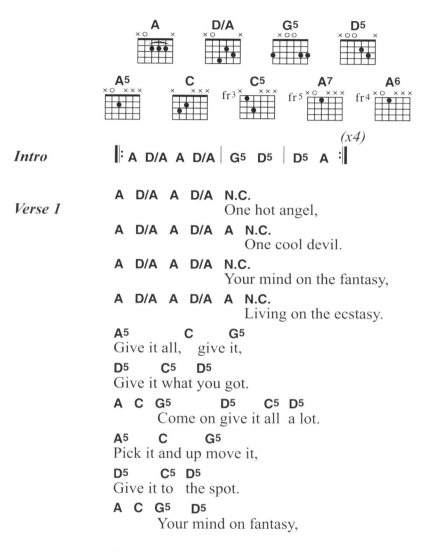

Intro
‖: A D/A A D/A | G5 D5 | D5 A :‖ *(x4)*

Verse 1

A D/A A D/A N.C.
One hot angel,

A D/A A D/A A N.C.
One cool devil.

A D/A A D/A N.C.
Your mind on the fantasy,

A D/A A D/A A N.C.
Living on the ecstasy.

A5   C   G5
Give it all,   give it,

D5   C5   D5
Give it what you got.

A C G5   D5   C5 D5
Come on give it all a lot.

A5   C   G5
Pick it and up move it,

D5   C5 D5
Give it to   the spot.

A C G5   D5
Your mind on fantasy,

Living on ecstasy.

Chorus 1

```
         A       D/A A   D/A   G5      D5      A
Run  -  a  -  way train, (running right off the track.)
             D/A A   D/A   G5      D5      A
Run  -  a  -  way train, (running right off the track.)
             D/A A   D/A   G5      D5      A
Run  -  a  -  way train, (running right off the track.)
                 D/A A   D/A   G5      D5      A
Yeah, the run  -  a  -  way train, (running right off the track.)
```

Verse 2

```
A  D/A  A  D/A  N.C.
               One hard ring a bell,
A  D/A  A  D/A  A  N.C.
                  Old school rebel.
A  D/A  A  D/A  N.C.
                 A ten for the revelry,
A  D/A  A  D/A  A  N.C.
                    Jamming up the agency.
A5         C  G5
Shake it,    shake it,
D5      C5  D5
Take it to   the spot.
A  C  G5             D5      C5    D5
       You know she make it real - ly hot.
A5          C  G5
Get it on, get it up,
D5         C5   D5
Come on give it all you got.
A  C  G5    D5
       Your mind on fantasy,

Living on the ecstasy.
```

Chorus 2

```
A      A/D A   A/D   G5      D5     A
Run  -  a  -  way train, (running right off the track.)
             A/D A   A/D   G5      D5     A
Yeah, the run  -  a  -  way train, (running right off the track.)
             A/D A   A/D   G5      D5     A
On the run  -  a  -  way train, (running right off the track.)
             A/D A   A/D   G5      D5     A
Run  -  a  -  way train, (running right off the track.)
```

Guitar solo

```
| A D/A A | G5 D5 | A D/A A | G5 D5 | A D/A A |

| G5 D5 | A      | N.C. | N.C. | N.C. | N.C. ||
```

Verse 3

A D/A A D/A N.C.
      One hot Southern belle,

A D/A A D/A A N.C.
        Son of a devil.

A D/A A D/A N.C.
      A school boy's spelling bee,

A D/A A D/A A N.C.
        A school girl and a fantasy.

A7 A6 A5
One hard ring a bell,

A7 A6 A5
All screwed up.

A7 A6 A5
A ten for the revelry,

A7 A6 A5
Jamming up the agency.

G5   D5
Shake it, shake it,

A
Take it to the spot.

G5 D5   A
You know she make it really hot, yeah.

G5   D5
Get it on, get it up,

A
Come on give it what you got.

G5 D5 A
You know she's just like a...

Chorus 3

A   D/A A D/A G5 D5   A
Run - a - way train,   she's coming off the track.

**   D/A A D/A   G5   D5 A**
Run - a - way train, yeah, (running right off the track.)

G5   D5
Get it on, get it up,

A
Come on give it all you got.

G5   D5 A
Runaway train,

G5   D5 A
(Running right off the track.)

G5   D5   A
Runaway train,

G5   D5 A   G5 D5 A
(Running right off the track.)

Rubber Lover

Words & Music by
Billy Joel, John Reid & Simon Neil

Gmaj7   A   D6   G5   A5   D5

Intro

‖: Gmaj7 A | D6 A | Gmaj7 A | D6 A :‖

| Gmaj7 A | D6 A | Gmaj7 A ‖

Verse 1

N.C.
Johnny had a pink rubber lover,

Pinned her to the roof of his house.

Went off and prophesied some good times,

A
Maybe he's just calling out.

Bridge 1

G5   A5   D5 A5
Funky all the way   home,
      G5   A5   D5   A5
It's regular except for the number.
G5   A5   D5 A5
Funky all the way   home,
                       A5   D5 A5
Funky all the way   home.

Chorus 1

Gmaj7 A D6   A   Gmaj7 A D6
Girl,   you're mak - ing me scream,
      A
My rub - ber lover,
Gmaj7 A D6   A   Gmaj7 A D6
Girl,   you're mak - ing me scream,
      A
My rub - ber lover.

Verse 2

G5   A5   D5   A5
Johnny had the ain of the lover,

G5   A5   D5   A
   Pinned her to the roof of his house.

     G5   A5   D5   A5
Went off and pro - phe - sied some good luck,

G5   A5 D5 A
Maybe he's just call - ing out.

Bridge 2

G5   A5   D5 A5
Funky all the way   home,

     G5   A5   D5   A5
It's regular except for the number.

G5   A5   D5 A5
Funky all the way   home,

G5   A5   D5
Funky all the way   home.

Link 1

| D6 Gmaj7 A | D6 Gmaj7 A ‖

Chorus 2

Gmaj7 A D6   A   Gmaj7   A D6
Girl,   you're mak - ing me scream,

            A
My rub - ber lover,

Gmaj7 A D6   A
Girl,   my rub - ber lover.

Link 2

| N.C. | N.C.   ‖
            A

Chorus 3

Gmaj7 A D6   A   Gmaj7   A D6
Girl,   you're mak - ing me scream,

            A
My rub - ber lover.

Gmaj7 A D6   A   Gmaj7   A D6
Girl,   you're mak - ing me scream,

            A
My rub - ber lover,

N.C.
Girl.

Rockets

Words & Music by
Gordon Goudie, James Kerr & Charles Burchill

| Am | F | G | Fsus2 | C | D7sus2 | E | Fmaj7 |

Intro

| Am | Am | Am | Am |

| F G | Am | F G | Am |

Verse 1

F   G Am
Your love's like faith,

F   G Am   F
Your love's spite in your eyes from those battle days.

         G Am
There's still one way,

F   G Am   Fsus2
Aban - doned now no matter what you say.

      G Am
Just one truth,

Fsus2   G Am   Fsus2
Moving up to decide that's your battle move.

      G Am
No one's here,

Fsus2   G Am   C
Some phan - toms realised that's your only fear.

Pre-chorus 1

C   D7sus2
You're sending me rockets,

       E
Full circle a - gain,

       Fmaj7 Am
More than I realised.

Chorus 1

Fsus2 G Am   Fsus2 G Am
             You're sending me ro - ckets,

           Fsus2 G Am
Full circle a - gain.

                  Fsus2 G Am
Still sending me ro - ckets.

Verse 2

F   G Am
   I could still cut through,

F   G   Am   F
   A war ma - chine with its missiles set on you.

      G   Am
I still want you,

F   G   Am   C
   Misty eyes clear to find another view.

Pre-chorus 2

(C)   D7sus2
   And still you're sending me rockets,

               E
And I surrender a - gain,

        Fmaj7
No more the key kills time.

Chorus 2

Fsus2 G Am   Fsus2 G Am
             You're sending me ro - ckets.

           Fsus2 G Am
Full circle a - gain.

                  Fsus2 G Am
Still sending me ro - ckets.

           Fmaj7
Full circle a - gain.

Verse 3

Fmaj⁷   **G Am**
Home sweet home,

Fmaj⁷ **G Am**   **Fmaj⁷**
No idea of di - vides or where the peace has gone.

   G Am
No words to blame,

Fmaj⁷ **G Am**   **C**
Surren - der leave me in the dark a - gain.

Pre-chorus 3

(C)   **D⁷sus²**
 You're sending me rockets,

    E
Full circle a - gain,

     Fmaj⁷ **Am**
More than I realised.

Link

| **Fsus² G** | **Am** | **Fsus² G** | **Am**   ‖

Chorus 3

(Am)   **Fsus² G Am** **Fsus² G Am**
 You're sending me ro - ckets.

      Fsus² G Am **Fsus² G Am**
Keep sending me ro - ckets.

      Fsus² G Am **Fsus² G Am**
Still sending me ro - ckets.

     Fsus² G Am
Full circle a - gain. *To fade*

Kings Of Leon

Sex On Fire

Words & Music by
Caleb Followill, Nathan Followill, Jared Followill & Matthew Followill

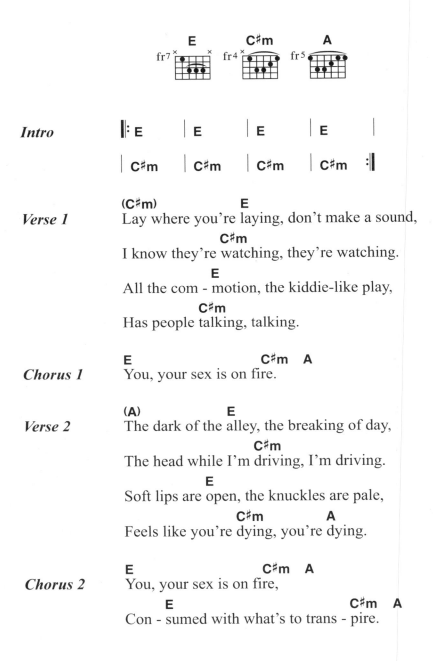

Intro ‖: E | E | E | E |
| C♯m | C♯m | C♯m | C♯m :‖

Verse 1
(C♯m)   E
Lay where you're laying, don't make a sound,
                  C♯m
I know they're watching, they're watching.

                E
All the com - motion, the kiddie-like play,
                C♯m
Has people talking, talking.

Chorus 1
E   C♯m   A
You, your sex is on fire.

Verse 2
(A)   E
The dark of the alley, the breaking of day,
                  C♯m
The head while I'm driving, I'm driving.

                E
Soft lips are open, the knuckles are pale,
                  C♯m   A
Feels like you're dying, you're dying.

Chorus 2
E   C♯m   A
You, your sex is on fire,
            E   C♯m   A
Con - sumed with what's to trans - pire.

Verse 3

       (A)   **E**
Hot as a fever, rattling bones,

           C♯m
I can just taste it, taste it.

                 E
If it's not for - ever, if it's just tonight,

                  C♯m   **A**
Oh, it's still the greatest, the greatest, the greatest.

Chorus 3

E   **C♯m** **A**
You, your sex is on fire.

       E   **C♯m**
And you, your sex is on fire,

         E   **C♯m** **A**
Con - sumed with what's to trans - pire.

Chorus 4

E   **C♯m** **A**
And you, your sex is on fire,

         E   **C♯m** **A E**
Con - sumed with what's to trans - pire.

Shine On

Words & Music by
Luke Pritchard

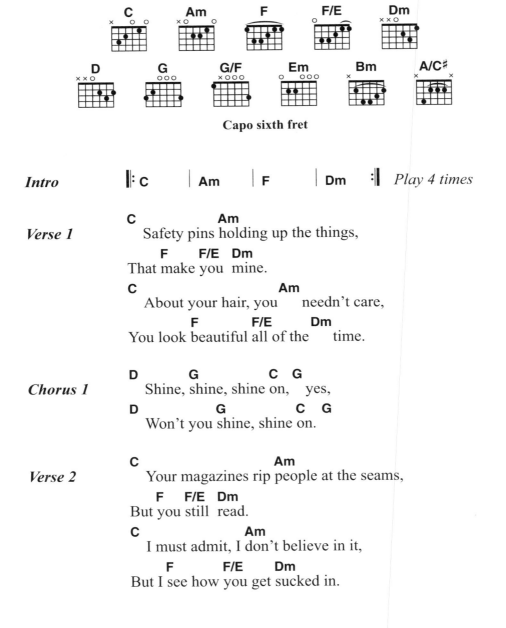

Capo sixth fret

Intro ‖: C | Am | F | Dm :‖ *Play 4 times*

Verse 1
   C   Am
   Safety pins holding up the things,
   F F/E Dm
That make you mine.
   C   Am
   About your hair, you needn't care,
     F   F/E   Dm
You look beautiful all of the time.

Chorus 1
   D   G   C G
   Shine, shine, shine on, yes,
   D   G   C G
   Won't you shine, shine on.

Verse 2
   C   Am
   Your magazines rip people at the seams,
    F F/E Dm
But you still read.
   C   Am
   I must admit, I don't believe in it,
    F   F/E   Dm
But I see how you get sucked in.

Chorus 2

    D   G   C G
    Shine, shine, shine on,   yes,

    D   G   C G
    Oh, won't you shine, shine on.

       G/F   D
    Sha, la, la, la.

       G   C G
    Shine, shine, shine on,   yes,

    D   G   Em
    Oh, won't you shine, shine on.

    G   G/F   Bm
    Because you're not done.

Bridge

    Bm A/C♯ D   C   G
                   Why do you bite the hand that feeds you?

    Why do you,

    D   C   Bm
    Why do you bite the hand that feeds you?

Instr.

    | C | Am | F F/E | Dm |

    | C | Am | F F/E | Dm | Dm   ‖

Chorus 3

    D   G   C G
    Shine, shine, shine on,   yes,

    D   G   C G
    Oh, won't you shine, shine on.

       G/F   D
    Sha, la, la, la.

       G   C G
    Shine, shine, shine on,   yes,

    D   G   Em G G/F
    Oh, won't you shine, shine on.

Verse 3

    C   Am
    Safety pins holding up the things,

       F   Dm
    That make you mine.

    C   Am
    About your hair, you   needn't care,

          F   Dm
    You look beautiful all of the   time.

Shock Of The Lightning

Words & Music by
Noel Gallagher

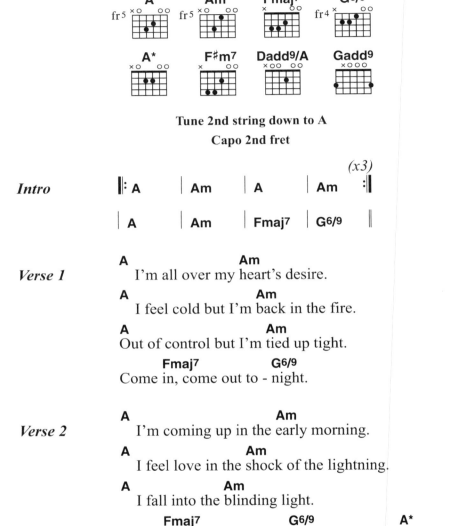

Tune 2nd string down to A

Capo 2nd fret

Intro
‖: A | Am | A | Am :‖ *(x3)*

| A | Am | Fmaj7 | G6/9 ‖

Verse 1

A   Am
I'm all over my heart's desire.

A   Am
I feel cold but I'm back in the fire.

A   Am
Out of control but I'm tied up tight.

Fmaj7   G6/9
Come in, come out to - night.

Verse 2

A   Am
I'm coming up in the early morning.

A   Am
I feel love in the shock of the lightning.

A   Am
I fall into the blinding light.

Fmaj7   G6/9   A*
Come in, come out, come in, come out to - night.

Chorus 1

F♯m7   **Fmaj7**
Love is a time machine,

F♯m7   **Dadd9/A**
Up on the silver screen.

A* **Dadd9/A**
It's all in my mind.

Fmaj7   **Dadd9/A**
Love is a litany,

Fmaj7   **Dadd9/A**
A magical mystery.

A* **Dadd9/A**
And all in good time.

A* **Dadd9/A**
And all in good time.

A* **Dadd9/A** | **Fmaj7** | **Gadd9** | **A*** | **A*** | **A*** | **A*** |
And all in good time._____

Verse 3

    A   **Am**
I got my feet on the street but I can't stop flying.

  A   **Am**
My head's in the clouds but at least I'm trying.

  A   **Am**
I'm out of control but I'm tied up tight.

    Fmaj7   **G6/9**
Come in, come out to - night.

Verse 4

    A   **Am**
There's a hole in the ground into which I'm falling.

A   **Am**
So God speed to the sound of the pounding.

A   **Am**
I'm all into the blinding light.

    Fmaj7   **G6/9**   **A**
Come in, come out, come in, come out to - night.

Chorus 2

F#m7   Fmaj7
Love is a time machine,

F#m7   Dadd9/A
Up on the silver screen.

A*   Dadd9/A
It's all in my mind.

Fmaj7   Dadd9/A
Love is a litany,

Fmaj7   Dadd9/A
A magical mystery.

A*   Dadd9/A
And all in good time.

A*   Dadd9/A
And all in good time.

A*   Dadd9/A | Fmaj7 | Gadd9 ‖
And all in good time._____

Instrumental

‖: A | Am | A | Am :‖ (x6)

| F#m7 | Fmaj7 | F#m7 | Dadd9/A |

Chorus 3

A*   Dadd9/A
It's all in my mind.

Fmaj7   Dadd9/A
Love is a time machine,

Fmaj7   Dadd9/A
Up on the silver screen.

A*   Dadd9/A
And all in good time.

A*   Dadd9/A
And all in good time.

A*   Dadd9/A | A* | Dadd9/A ‖
And all in good time._____

Outro

‖: A* | Dadd9/A | A* | Dadd9/A :‖ (x4)

| A* ‖

Sick Muse

Words & Music by
James Shaw, Emily Haines & Gavin Brown

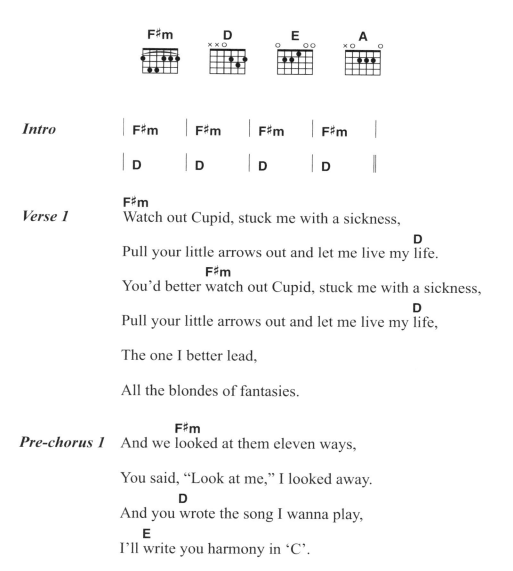

Intro | F♯m | F♯m | F♯m | F♯m |

| D | D | D | D ||

Verse 1

    F♯m
Watch out Cupid, stuck me with a sickness,

                                  D
Pull your little arrows out and let me live my life.

               F♯m
You'd better watch out Cupid, stuck me with a sickness,

                                D
Pull your little arrows out and let me live my life,

The one I better lead,

All the blondes of fantasies.

Pre-chorus 1

            F♯m
And we looked at them eleven ways,

You said, "Look at me," I looked away.

         D
And you wrote the song I wanna play,

       E
I'll write you harmony in 'C'.

Chorus 1
   E   A
Everybody, everybody just wanna fall in love.

            E
Everybody, everybody just wanna play the lead.

         A
Everybody, everybody just wanna fall in love,

            E
Everybody, everybody just wanna play the lead,

Play the lead, play the lead.

Link 1
| F♯m | F♯m | F♯m | F♯m |

| D | D | D | D ‖

Verse 2
   F♯m
Watch out Cupid, money is a sick muse,

                                        D
Pull your little arrows out and let me live my life.

            F♯m
She said, "I'm with stupid, money is a sick muse,

                                       D
Pull your little arrows out and let me live my life."

The one I better lead,

All the blondes of fantasies.

Pre-chorus 2 As Pre-chorus 1

Chorus 2   As Chorus 1

Bridge 1
  A
Ah, ah, ah, ah, ah, ah, ah.

Ah, ah, ah, ah, ah, ah, ah.

Link 2

| F♯m | F♯m | F♯m | F♯m | |
| D | D | D | D | |

E
I'll write you harmony in 'C'.

Chorus 3   As Chorus 1

A
Outro   Ah, ah, ah, ah, ah, ah, ah.

Ah, ah, ah, ah, ah, ah, ah.

Skinny Love

Words & Music by
Justin Vernon

⑥ = C ③ = G
⑤ = G ② = C
④ = E ① = C

Am **C** fr5 **C***

D13(no 3) fr7 **C(add9/E)** fr7 **G(add11)/B** **F/A**

Tune guitar slightly flat

Intro

‖: Am | C | C* | C* :‖ *Play 3 times*

| D13(no 3) | D13(no 3) | Am | Am C |

| C* | C* | C* | C* ‖

Verse 1

Am   C   C*
Come on skinny love just last the year,
Am   C   C*
Pour a little salt we were never here.
               Am   C   C*
My, my, my, my, my, my, my, my,
                     D13(no 3)   Am
Staring at the sink of blood and crushed veneer.

Link 1

| C | C | C | C ‖

Verse 2

Am   C   C*
 I tell my love to wreck it all,
Am   C   C*
Cut out all the ropes and let me fall.
               Am   C   C*
My, my, my, my, my, my, my, my,
                     D13(no 3)   Am
Right in this   moment this order's tall.

Chorus 1

C(add9)/E
And I told you to be patient,

G(add11)/B　　**F/A**
And I told you to be fine.

C(add9)/E
And I told you to be balanced,

G(add11)/B　　**F/A**
And I told you to be kind.

　C(add9)/E
And in the morning I'll be with you,

　　G(add11)/B　　**F/A**
But it will be a different kind.

　　C(add9)/E
And I'll be holding all the tickets,

　　G(add11)/B　　**F/A**
And you'll be owning all the fines.

Verse 3

Am　　　　　**C**　　　　　　**C***
Come on skinny love what happened here?

Am　　　　**C**　　　　　**C***
Suckle on the hope in light bras - sieres,

　　Am　　　**C**　　　**C***
My, my, my, my, my, my, my, my,

　　　D13(no 3)　　　　**Am**　　**F/A**
Sullen load is full; so slow on the split.

Chorus 2

      C(add9)/E
And I told you to be patient,

      G(add11)/B   **F/A**
And I told you to be fine.

      C(add9)/E
And I told you to be balanced,

      G(add11)/B   **F/A**
And I told you to be kind.

        C(add9)/E
And now all your love is wasted,

        G(add11)/B   **F/A**
And then who the hell was I?

        C(add9)/E
And I'm breaking at the britches,

        G(add11)/B   **F/A**
And at the end of all your lines.

Bridge

C(add9)/E
  Who will love you?

G(add11)/B **F/A**
  Who will fight?

C(add9)/E   **G(add11)/B**   **F/A**
  Who will fall_____ far be - hind?

Outro

‖: **Am** | **C** | **C*** | **C*** :‖ *Play 3 times*

| **D13(no 3)** | **D13(no 3)** | **Am** | **Am** **C** | **C**   ‖

Seasick Steve

Started Out With Nothin'

Words & Music by
Steve Wold

⑥ = D   ③ = F♯   D   G⁷/D   F   fr5 G   D7
⑤ = A   ② = A
④ = D   ① = D

riff 1

D	D	A	C	A	G	F♯	F	D
0fr	5fr	0fr	3fr	3fr	1fr	0fr	3fr	0fr
⑥	②	②	②	②	③	③	⑥	④

Intro

Riff reference

riff 2

D	F♯	D	C	A	G	F♯	F	D
0fr	4fr	0fr	3fr	3fr	1fr	0fr	3fr	0fr
⑥	①	①	②	②	③	③	⑥	④

Verse 1

        D (riff 1)   **riff 2**
I can't lose what I never had,

        riff 2   **riff 2**
And you can't take what I ain't got.

      riff 2   **riff 2**
When I'm happy, you won't make me sad,

        riff 2   **riff 2**
Depending on you all, well I'm not.

Riff reference

riff 3

A	B	F	F	D	A	B	A	B
0fr	2fr	3fr	3fr	0fr	0fr	2fr	0fr	2fr
②	②	①	①	①	②	②	②	②

Chorus 1

   D (riff 3)
'Cause I started out with nothing,

      G⁷/D   **F**   **riff 1** *(x2)*
And I've still got most of it left.

Verse 2

        D (riff 2)   **riff 2**
When I'm down I just get up,

        riff 2   **riff 2**
When I'm down, well I stand up.

        riff 2   **riff 2**
Been down many times, well you know it's true,

        riff 2   **riff 2**
Haven't had a red dime between me and you.

Chorus 2

   D (riff 3)
'Cause I started out with nothing,

        G⁷/D   **F**   **riff 1***(x2)*
And I've still got most of it left.

     G
'Cause I started out with nothing,

        F   **riff 1***(x2)*
And I've still got most of it left.

     G
Yes I started out with nothing,

        F   **riff 1***(x2)*
And I've still got most of it left.

Guitar solo   ‖: D | D | D | D   :‖ *Play 4 times*

Chorus 3

     G
Well I started out with nothing,

        F   **riff 1***(x2)*
And I've still got most of it left.

     G
Yes I started out with nothing,

        F   **riff 1***(x2)*
And I've still got most of it left.

Verse 3

        D (riff 2)   **riff 2**
And if it all fell apart to - day,

        riff 2   **riff 2**
I could just walk, get on down the street.

        riff 2   **riff 2**
I ain't worried where I'm going to sleep,

        riff 2   **riff 2**
I can always find some food to eat.

Chorus 4

G
Because I started out with nothing,

                F   **riff 1** *(x2)*
And I've still got most of it left.

G
Well I started out with nothing,

                F   **riff 1**
And I've still got most of it left.

          riff 1
Most of it left,

              riff 1
Got most of it left,

          riff 1
Most of it left.

Outro

D (riff 3)
Because I started out with nothing,

          G7/D   **F**   **D7**
And I've still got most of it left.

Stormy High

Words & Music by
Matthew Camirand, Stephen McBean,
Jeremy Schmidt & Amber Webber

| Am | Asus4 | Asus2 | E5 | F♯5 | A5 |
| B5 | C♯5 | D♯5 | F♯ | A | B |

Intro

| Am | Asus4 | Am | Asus2 ‖

‖: E5 | E5 | E5 | E5 :‖ *Play 3 times*

| F♯5 | F♯5 | F♯5 | F♯5 ‖

| E5 | E5 | E5 | E5 ‖

E5
Oh, oh, oh, oh.

Oh, oh, oh, oh.

Oh, oh, oh, oh.

Oh, oh, oh, oh.

Verse 1

F♯5
   Witches on your trail, my lord,

Stormy, stormy high.

You've been dying to be set free,

                       A5 B5
Oh, curse those hunting hounds.

Link

E5
Oh, oh, oh, oh.

Oh, oh, oh, oh.

Verse 2

F#5
   It wasn't the doctors who fed us the pills,

Watch for the ones who don't crack.

C#5
   But they're dangerous like barbed wire toys,

F#5   A5 B5
Oh, stormy, stormy minds.

Instr.

‖: E5 | E5 | E5 | E5 :‖

| F#5 | F#5 | A5 | A5 |

| B5 | B5 | C#5 | C#5 |

| D#5 | D#5 | E ‖

‖: E5 | E5 | E5 | E5 :‖ *Play 3 times*

Verse 3

E5   C#5
Well, oh, it wasn't arson which drove us to flames,

                       F#5
Frightened daughters of old.

Oh, well you've been up since the lights burnt down,

C#5
Oh, you've been up for so long,

A5 E5 B5   F#5
Oh._____

Bridge

F#
   A-stormy, stormy high.

A
  A-stormy, stormy high.

B
  A-stormy, stormy high.

F#
   A-stormy, stormy high.

F#
   A-stormy, stormy high.

A
  A-stormy, stormy high.

B
  A-stormy, stormy high.

146

cont.

F#
A-stormy, stormy high.

F#
A-stormy, stormy high.

A
  A-stormy, stormy high.

B   **C#5** **D#5**
A-stormy, stormy high.

Outro | E5 | E5 | E5 | E5 |

              | E5 | E5 | E5 | E5 A5 B5 | E5 ||

Take Back The City

Words & Music by
Paul Wilson, Gary Lightbody,
Jonathan Quinn, Nathan Connolly & Tom Simpson

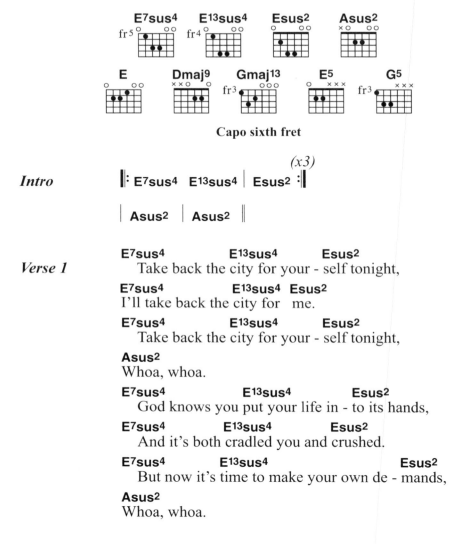

Capo sixth fret

Intro ‖: E7sus4 E13sus4 | Esus2 :‖ *(x3)*

| Asus2 | Asus2 ‖

Verse 1

E7sus4   E13sus4   Esus2
Take back the city for your - self tonight,

E7sus4   E13sus4 Esus2
I'll take back the city for me.

E7sus4   E13sus4   Esus2
Take back the city for your - self tonight,

Asus2
Whoa, whoa.

E7sus4   E13sus4   Esus2
God knows you put your life in - to its hands,

E7sus4   E13sus4   Esus2
And it's both cradled you and crushed.

E7sus4   E13sus4   Esus2
But now it's time to make your own de - mands,

Asus2
Whoa, whoa.

Verse 2

E⁷sus⁴   **E¹³sus⁴**   **Esus²**
All these years later and it's killing me,

E⁷sus⁴   **E¹³sus⁴**   **Esus²**
Your broken records and words.

E⁷sus⁴   **E¹³sus⁴**   **Esus²**
Ten thousand craters where it all should be,

Asus²
Whoa, whoa.

E⁷sus⁴   **E¹³sus⁴**   **Esus²**
No need to put your words in - to my mouth,

E⁷sus⁴   **E¹³sus⁴**   **Esus²**
Don't need con - vincing at all.

E⁷sus⁴   **E¹³sus⁴**   **Esus²**
I love this place enough to have no doubt,

Asus²
Whoa, whoa.

Pre-chorus 1

(Asus²)   **E**   **Dmaj⁹**
It's a mess, it's a start,

      Asus²   **Gmaj¹³**
It's a flawed work of art.

      E   **Dmaj⁹**
Your city, your call,

      Asus²   **Gmaj¹³**
Every crack,   every wall.

      E   **Dmaj⁹**
Pick a side, pick a fight,

      Asus²   **Gmaj¹³**
Get your epitaph right.

      E   **Dmaj⁹**
You can sing till you drop,

      Asus²   **Gmaj¹³**
'Cause the fun just never stops.

Chorus 1

E⁵   **G⁵**
I love this city to - night,

      Asus²
I love this city always.

E⁵   **G⁵**
It bears its teeth like a light,

      Asus²
And spits me out aft - er days.

cont.

E5   G5
  But we're all gluttons for it,

            Asus2
We know it's wrong and it's right.

E5   G5
  For every time it's been hit,

          Asus2
Take back the city tonight.

Guitar solo ‖: E7sus4 E13sus4 | Esus2 :‖

       | Asus2 | Asus2 ‖

Verse 3

E7sus4   E13sus4 Esus2
  Tell me you never wanted more than this,

E7sus4   E13sus4 Esus2
  And I will stop talking now.

E7sus4   E13sus4   Esus2
  One perfect partner, one e - ternal kiss,

Asus2
Whoa, whoa.

E7sus4   E13sus4   Esus2
  Take back the city for your - self tonight,

E7sus4   E13sus4 Esus2
I'll take back the city for me.

E7sus4   E13sus4   Esus2
  Take back the city for your - self tonight,

Asus2
Whoa, whoa.

Chorus 2 As Chorus 1

Chorus 3 As Chorus 1

Outro

E5   G5
  I love this city to - night,

           Asus2
I love this city al - ways.

E5   N.C.
  I love this city to - night,

I love this city always.

That's Not My Name

Words & Music by
Katie White & Jules De Martino

Intro | N.C. | N.C. | N.C. | N.C. ‖

Verse 1

E5
Four little words just to get me along,

It's a difficulty and I'm biting on my tongue and I,

I keep stalling, and keeping me together,

People around gotta find something to say now.

A5
Holding back, everyday the same,

Don't wanna be a loner,

Listen to me, oh no.

I never say anything at all,

                                                       B5   **N.C.**
But with nothing to consider they forget my name, ame, ame, ame.

Chorus 1

N.C.   E5
They call me 'Hell', they call me 'Stacey',

They call me 'Her', they call me 'Jane'.

          A5
That's not my name, that's not my name,

That's not my name, that's not my name.

B5   E5
   They call me 'Quiet Girl', but I'm a riot.

Mary-Jo-Lisa, always the same.

          A5
That's not my name, that's not my name,

                B5
That's not my name, that's not my name.

Verse 2

E5
   I miss the catch if they throw me the ball,

I'm the last chick standing up against the wall.

Keep up, falling, these heels they keep me boring,

Getting clamped up and sitting on the fence now.

A5
   So alone all the time and I,

Lock myself away,

Listen to me, oh no.

Although I'm dressed up, out and all with,

                          B5   N.C.
Everything considered they forget my name, ame, ame, ame.

Chorus 2   As Chorus 1

Bridge 1

E5   A5   B5
Are you calling me darling?

E5   A5   B5
Are you calling me bird?

E5   A5   B5
Are you calling me darling?

E5   A5   B5
Are you calling me bird?

Chorus 3   As Chorus 1

Chorus 4   As Chorus 1

Chorus 5   As Chorus 1

Vocals ad lib.

Outro

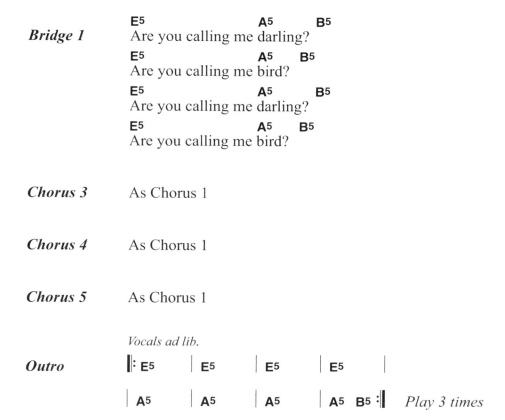

‖: E5 | E5 | E5 | E5 |

| A5 | A5 | A5 | A5 B5 :‖   *Play 3 times*

Time To Pretend

Words & Music by
Andrew Vanwyngarden & Benjamin Goldwasser

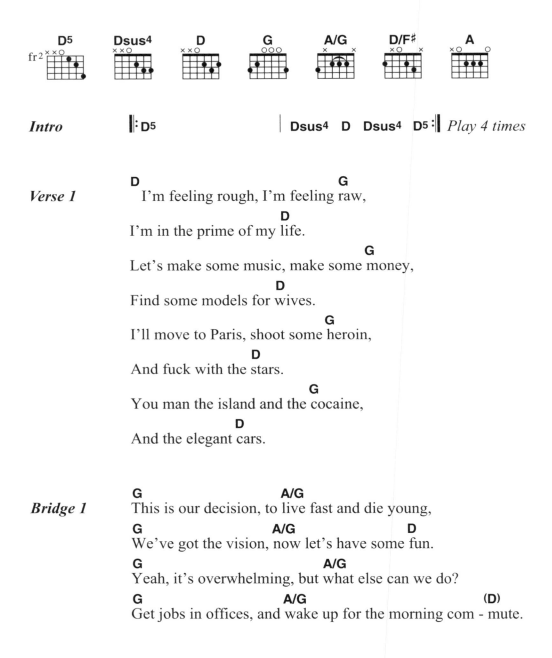

Intro ‖: **D5** | **Dsus4** **D** **Dsus4** **D5** :‖ *Play 4 times*

Verse 1

      D   **G**
I'm feeling rough, I'm feeling raw,

                     D
I'm in the prime of my life.

                                   G
Let's make some music, make some money,

                     D
Find some models for wives.

                              G
I'll move to Paris, shoot some heroin,

                     D
And fuck with the stars.

                             G
You man the island and the cocaine,

                     D
And the elegant cars.

Bridge 1

G   **A/G**
This is our decision, to live fast and die young,

G   **A/G**   **D**
We've got the vision, now let's have some fun.

G   **A/G**
Yeah, it's overwhelming, but what else can we do?

G   **A/G**   **(D)**
Get jobs in offices, and wake up for the morning com - mute.

Link 1

D		D	

(- mute)

D		D	

Chorus 1

A   D/F♯
Forget about our mothers and our friends,

          G   A   D
We're fated to pre - tend.

G   D
  To pre - tend,

         G   D
We're fated to pre - tend,

G   D   G
  To pre - tend.

Verse 2

D   G
  I'll miss the playgrounds and the animals,

                    D
And digging up worms.

                             G
I'll miss the comfort of my mother,

                       D
And the weight of the world.

                            G
I'll miss my sister, miss my father,

                    D
Miss my dog and my home.

                               G
Yeah, I'll miss the boredom and the freedom,

                    D
And the time spent a - lone.

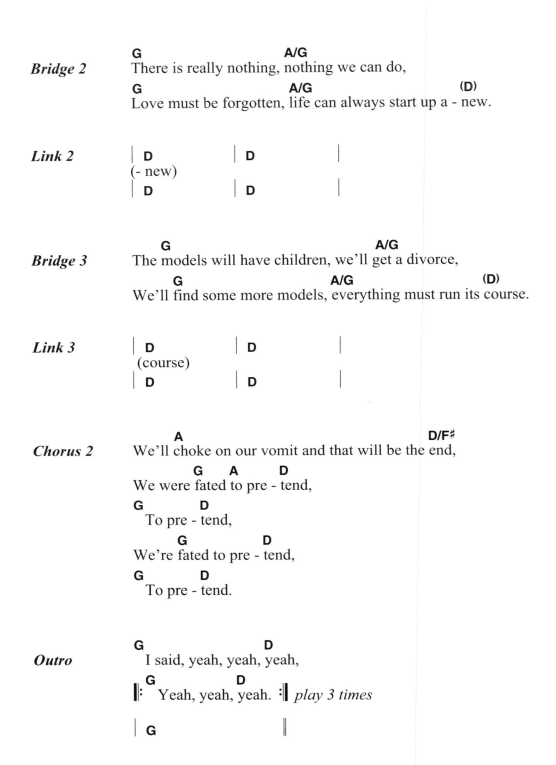

Bridge 2

    G   A/G
There is really nothing, nothing we can do,

    G   A/G   (D)
Love must be forgotten, life can always start up a - new.

Link 2

| D | D | |

(- new)

| D | D | |

Bridge 3

        G   A/G
The models will have children, we'll get a divorce,

        G   A/G   (D)
We'll find some more models, everything must run its course.

Link 3

| D | D | |

(course)

| D | D | |

Chorus 2

        A   D/F♯
We'll choke on our vomit and that will be the end,

             G   A   D
We were fated to pre - tend,

    G   D
  To pre - tend,

             G   D
We're fated to pre - tend,

    G   D
  To pre - tend.

Outro

    G   D
  I said, yeah, yeah, yeah,

‖: G   D
    Yeah, yeah, yeah. :‖ *play 3 times*

| G | ‖

MGMT

To Lose My Life

Words & Music by
Harry McVeigh, Charles Cave & Jack Brown

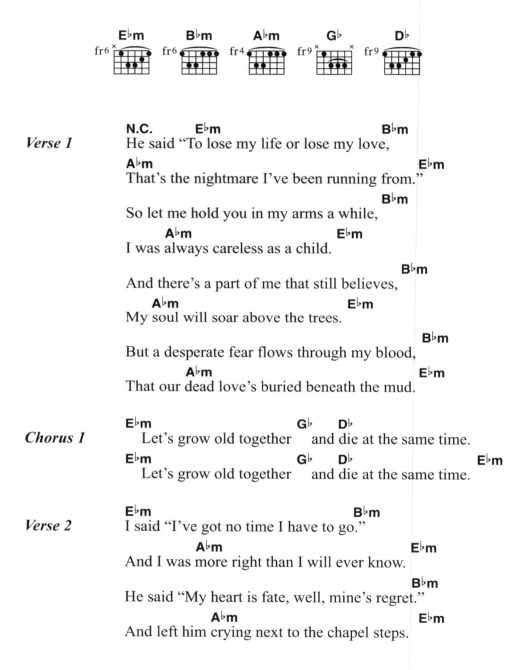

Verse 1

N.C.   E♭m   B♭m
He said "To lose my life or lose my love,
A♭m   E♭m
That's the nightmare I've been running from."

                                          B♭m
So let me hold you in my arms a while,
            A♭m   E♭m
I was always careless as a child.

And there's a part of me that still believes,   B♭m
            A♭m   E♭m
My soul will soar above the trees.

                                         B♭m
But a desperate fear flows through my blood,
            A♭m   E♭m
That our dead love's buried beneath the mud.

Chorus 1

E♭m   G♭   D♭
   Let's grow old together   and die at the same time.
E♭m   G♭   D♭   E♭m
   Let's grow old together   and die at the same time.

Verse 2

E♭m   B♭m
I said "I've got no time I have to go."
            A♭m   E♭m
And I was more right than I will ever know.

                                        B♭m
He said "My heart is fate, well, mine's regret."
            A♭m   E♭m
And left him crying next to the chapel steps.

Chorus 2

E♭m   G♭   D♭
Let's grow old together   and die at the same time.

E♭m   G♭   D♭
Let's grow old together   and die at the same time.

   E♭m
He said,

                        G♭   D♭
"Let's grow old together   and die at the same time.

                        G♭
Let's grow old together   and die at the same time."

   (B♭m)
He said.

Bridge

| B♭m | B♭m | B♭m | B♭m ‖

B♭m
He said, "To lose my life or lose my love,

That's the nightmare I've been running from."

Outro

With chorus lyrics sung underneath

(B♭m)   E♭m
So let me hold you in my arms a while,

G♭   D♭
I was careless as a child.

      E♭m
There's a part of me that still believes,

    G♭   D♭
My soul will soar a - bove the trees.

   E♭m
A desperate fear flows through my blood,

    G♭   D♭
Our dead love's buried be - neath the mud.

   E♭m
A desperate fear flows through my blood,

    G♭   D♭
Our dead love's buried be - neath the mud.

            E♭m
(Die at the same time.)

Tonight's Today

Words & Music by
Paul Epworth & Jack Peñate

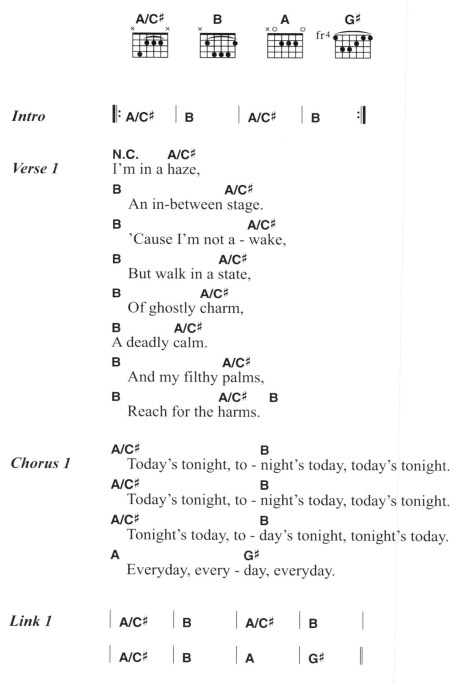

Intro ‖: A/C♯ | B | A/C♯ | B :‖

Verse 1

N.C.   A/C♯
I'm in a haze,

B   A/C♯
An in-between stage.

B   A/C♯
'Cause I'm not a - wake,

B   A/C♯
But walk in a state,

B   A/C♯
Of ghostly charm,

B   A/C♯
A deadly calm.

B   A/C♯
And my filthy palms,

B   A/C♯   B
Reach for the harms.

Chorus 1

A/C♯   B
Today's tonight, to - night's today, today's tonight.

A/C♯   B
Today's tonight, to - night's today, today's tonight.

A/C♯   B
Tonight's today, to - day's tonight, tonight's today.

A   G♯
Everyday, every - day, everyday.

Link 1 | A/C♯ | B | A/C♯ | B |

| A/C♯ | B | A | G♯ ‖

Verse 2

A/C♯   B
Tonight just be - came this morning,
A/C♯   B
The sun's waves at the moon.
A/C♯   B
The thought has just started dawning,
                 A   G♯
That there's still so much more that I can do.
A/C♯   B
I shuffle into the sunlight,
A/C♯   B
A zombie roaming on the day.
A/C♯   B
She looks at me and says, "What a sight."
A   B
A passing woman says.

Chorus 2

A/C♯   B
Today's tonight, to - night's today, today's tonight.
A/C♯   B
Today's tonight, to - night's today, today's tonight.
A/C♯   B
Tonight's today, to - day's tonight, tonight's today.
A   G♯
Every night's the same.

Bridge

(G♯)   A   G♯
I'm ringing church bells, church bells,
                   A/C♯ B
I'm ringing church bells.
            A   G♯
I'm ringing church bells, church bells,
                   A/C♯
I'm ringing church bells,
            B
I'm ringing bells.

Chorus 3   As Chorus 1

Chorus 4   As Chorus 1

Chorus 5   As Chorus 1

Too Fake

Words & Music by
Benjamin Grubin

B♭m7 (fr6) **D♭** (fr4) **G♭** (fr9) **E♭m** (fr6) **A♭** (fr11) **Ddim** (fr4)

Intro ‖: B♭m7 | B♭m7 | B♭m7 | B♭m7 :‖

Verse 1

B♭m7
I'd do anything that I'm told to,

I'd even mean it if I'm supposed to.

Lead me on a little, I go for broke,

Lead me on some more, I'd go for the big joke.

Everybody's watching, oh, but nobody cares, no.

Oh wait, does it go, huh?

Nobody's watching, but everybody cares,

Oh whatever, I'll talk to you later.

Chorus 1

       D♭   G♭   B♭m7
Look out, 'cause I'm just too fake for the world,
      E♭m   D♭
Ah, you know it's just a game to me.
      G♭   E♭m
I'm just too fake you see,
  A♭
I wish I didn't have to be.
    D♭   G♭   B♭m7
But watch out, I got too much soul for the world,
    E♭m   D♭
It's breaking my heart in two.
    Ddim   E♭m
Well, I got too much soul for you,
   A♭
I don't like it but it's true.

Verse 2

B♭m7
  Get off.

I'll go to church if I'm expected to,

I'll be a lost soul if they need examples to use.

I could stay forever, leave right now, it's your call either way,

It's time to use my life for myself.

Most people just won't tell you that.

I'm gonna use my life for someone else, yeah.

No wait, wait, wait, wait.

Chorus 2

     D♭   **G♭**   **B♭m7**
Look out, 'cause I'm just too fake for the world,
     E♭m   **D♭**
Ah, you know it's just a game to me.
       G♭   **E♭m**
I'm just too fake you see,
   A♭
I wish I didn't have to be.
    D♭   **G♭**   **B♭m7**
But oh, I got too much soul for the world,
     E♭m   **D♭**
And it's breaking my heart in two.
     Ddim   **E♭m**
Well, I got too much soul for you,
    A♭
I don't like it but it's true.

Verse 3

B♭m7
  Hurts right?

But I can't even talk to you,

About my effect on people.

'Cause I'm doing the same thing to you,

That's right, even right now.

Oh just wait up for me if you want to but...

Chorus 3

D♭   G♭   B♭m7
Look out now, I'm just too fake for the world,

      E♭m   D♭
Ah, you know it's just a game to me.

  G♭   E♭m
I'm just too fake you see,

  A♭
I hope you can forgive me.

D♭   G♭   B♭m7
Oh now, I got too much soul for the world,

     E♭m   D♭
And it's breaking my heart in two.

    Ddim   E♭m
Well, I got too much soul for you,

    A♭
I don't like it but it's true.

Chorus 4

D♭   G♭   B♭m7
Look out now, well I'm just too fake for the world,

   E♭m   D♭
And it's just that I could do without it.

  G♭   E♭m
No, I'm   just too fake for you,

  A♭
I don't like it but it's true.

  D♭ G♭   B♭m7
Look out, I got too much soul for the world,

E♭m   D♭
It's breaking my heart in two.

  Ddim   E♭m
Well, I got too much soul for you,

  A♭
I don't like it but it's true.

Outro

  D♭   G♭   B♭m7
Look out, I'm just too fake for the world,

E♭m   D♭
I know it's just a game to me.

  G♭   B♭m7
I'm just too fake you see,

 A♭
I hope you could forgive me.

  D♭
Look out now, too fake.

True No. 9 Blues

Words & Music by
Gwilym Gold

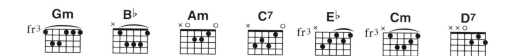

Intro

Gm
(True Romance)

(True Romance)

Verse 1

Gm
Take time to hear the Bow bells ring,

Never turn your back on love never, never, never let it in.

B♭
Swing   like Art Tatum, shoot your lover down, shine your shoes.
Gm
Watch out! Keep your windows down, tomorrow it could be you.
Am
Get out of bed, get ahead, get a hat,

Read the rags, read the news.
C7
Stay in fashion, make some cash,

You've really got nothing left to lose.

Chorus 1

           Gm
(True Ro - mance)

Find a new romance,
        E♭
(True Ro - mance)

Another true romance,
Cm
Give yourself another chance,
             Gm
Forgive your brothers and sisters.
D7   **B♭**
Find some time for tea and wine and Valentines,
    C7   **Gm**
For - get about the big picture.

Verse 2

           Gm
(True Ro - mance)

Make time to get lucky and find favour with the freaks.

Be a fabulous weekend wonder and a miracle worker in the week.
B♭
You are a genius everyday but don't lose your common touch.
Gm
Join a gang, learn rhyming slang,

Learn Greek, learn double Dutch.
Am
Get a car, get a job, get a girl, pay your taxes, pay your bills.
C7
Pull yourself out of the water boy, God knows no one else will.

Chorus 2   As Chorus 1

Instr.   ‖: Gm | Gm | Gm | Gm :‖

166

Verse 3

Gm
Join a Mercury cult, join a suicide pact,

Smoke more, stop the war, make more folk lore.

I think my heart might be the new black!

All the myths and legends are under attack.

B♭
So I'll   buy some lunar land,

Buy a ticket for a daytrip to the moon.

Gm
Keep one eye on the boys of summer,

And drink in the afternoon.

Am
Get on - line! Get in line!

Read between the lines, straighten up your facts.

C7
Stamp your post with Penny Blacks,

Rule Britannia ain't coming back.

Chorus 3   As Chorus 1

Chorus 4   As Chorus 1

Outro
                    Gm
(True Ro - mance)

                    E♭   **Cm Gm D7 B**♭ **C7 Gm**
(True Ro - mance)

167

Two Weeks

Words & Music by
Christopher Taylor, Christopher Bear, Edward Droste & Daniel Rossen

| F | Am/E | C | B♭6 | B♭ | F6 | Gm6 | Gm |

Intro | F | Am/E C |

| F | Am/E C | F | Am/E C |
Oh._____

| F | Am/E C ‖
Oh.____

Verse 1

F   Am/E   C
Save up all the days,

F   Am/E   C
A routine ma - laise.

F   Am/E
Just like yester - day,

  C   F   Am/E C
I told you I would stay.

Chorus 1

(C)   B♭6 B♭   F6 F Gm6 Gm
Would you al - ways,

         B♭6   B♭   F6 F Gm6 Gm
Maybe some - times,

    B♭6 B♭ F6 F Gm6 Gm
Make it ea - sy,

     B♭6   B♭ F6 F Gm6 Gm
Take your time.

Link 1 | F | Am/E C | F | Am/E C ‖
Oh.____

Verse 2

F   Am/E   C
Think of all the ways,

F   Am/E   C
Momentary phase.

F   Am/E
Just like yester - day,

  C   F Am/E C
I told you I would stay.

Verse 3

```
F              Am/E  C
```
Every time you try,
```
F              Am/E  C
```
Quarter half a mile.
```
F              Am/E
```
Just like yester - day,
```
 C              F    Am/E  C
```
I told you I would   stay.

Link 2   ‖ B♭6 B♭ ‖ F6 F Gm6 Gm │ B♭6 B♭ ‖ F6 F Gm6 Gm ‖

Chorus 2

```
(Gm)      B♭6  B♭   F6  F  Gm6  Gm
```
Would you al - ways,
```
      B♭6      B♭   F6  F  Gm6  Gm
```
Maybe some - times,
```
      B♭6 B♭  F6  F  Gm6  Gm
```
Make it ea - sy,
```
      B♭6    B♭  F6  F  Gm6  Gm
```
Take your time.

Chorus 3

```
(Gm)      (B♭)     (F)  (Gm6)
```
Would you always,
```
      (B♭)        (F)  (Gm6)
```
Maybe sometimes,
```
      B♭6 B♭  F6  F  Gm6  Gm
```
Make it ea - sy,
```
      B♭6    B♭  F6  F  Gm6  Gm
```
Take your time.
```
B♭6  B♭    F6  F  Gm6  Gm
```
Al - ways,
```
B♭6      B♭    F6  F  Gm6  Gm
```
Some - times,
```
B♭6 B♭   F6  F  Gm6  Gm
```
Ea - sy,
```
B♭6    B♭  F6  F  Gm6  Gm
```
Time.

Outro   │ F   │ Am/E C │ F   │ Am/E C │
                                        Oh._____

          │ F   │ Am/E C │ F   │ Am/E C ‖
                                        Oh._____

Use Somebody

Words & Music by
Caleb Followill, Nathan Followill, Jared Followill & Matthew Followill

C5   Em   F5   A5   D5   F♯5   B

Intro

C5 Em F5
Oh, oh._____

C5 Em F5
Oh, oh._____

A5 C5 F5
Oh, oh._____

A5 C5 F5
Oh, oh._____

Verse 1

(F5)   C5   Em   F5
I've been roaming around,__ always looking down,__ at all I see.____

                 C5   Em   F5
Painted fa - ces fill the pla - ces I can't reach.____

                                      A5   C5   F5
You know that I could use somebody,____

                                      A5   C5   F5
You know that I could use somebody.

Verse 2

                              C5   Em   F5
Someone like you,__ and all you know,__ and how you speak.__

                 C5   Em   F5
Countless lov - ers under cov - er of the street.____

                                      A5   C5   F5
You know that I could use somebody,

                                      A5   C5   F5
You know that I could use somebody,

Someone like you.

Chorus

C5 Em F5
Oh, oh._____

C5 Em F5
Oh, oh._____

A5 C5 F5
Oh, oh._____

A5 C5 F5
Oh, oh._____

Verse 3

(C5)   (Em)   (F5)
Off in the night,___ while you live it up,___ I'm off to sleep.___

(C5)   (Em)   (F5)
Waging wars___ to shake the po - et and the beat.___

A5   C5 F5
I hope it's gonna make you notice,

A5   C5 F5
I hope it's gonna make you notice,

Someone like me.

Chorus 2

C5 Em F5
Oh, oh._____ (Someone like me.)

C5 Em F5
Oh, oh._____ (Someone like me,

A5 C5 F5
Oh, oh._____
  somebody.)

A5 C5 F5
Oh, oh._____

Bridge

D5   F♯
 Go and let it out, go and let it out,

       D5
Go and let it out, go and let it out,

       F♯
Go and let it out, go and let it out,

  B
Go and let it out.

Solo

|C5 |Em |F5 |F5 |

C5 Em F5
Oh, oh._____ Someone like you,

A5   C5 F5
 somebody,_____ someone like you,

A5   C5 F5
 somebody._____

Outro

(F5)   C5   Em   F5
I've been roaming around,__ always looking down,__ at all I see.___

Viva La Vida

Words & Music by
Guy Berryman, Chris Martin, Jon Buckland & Will Champion

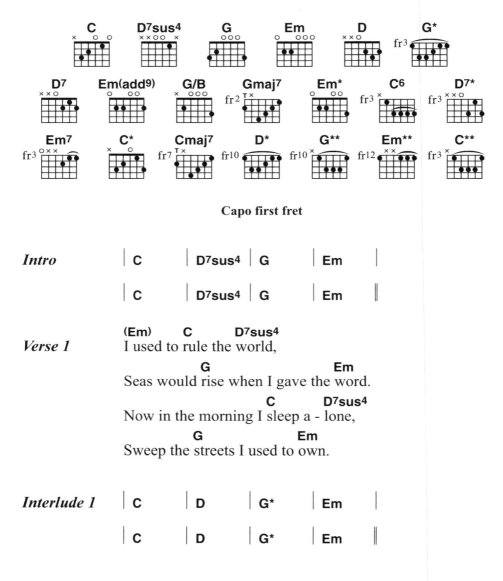

Capo first fret

Intro

| C | D⁷sus⁴ | G | Em |

| C | D⁷sus⁴ | G | Em |

Verse 1

(Em)   C   D⁷sus⁴
I used to rule the world,

       G   Em
Seas would rise when I gave the word.

          C   D⁷sus⁴
Now in the morning I sleep a - lone,

       G   Em
Sweep the streets I used to own.

Interlude 1

| C | D | G* | Em |

| C | D | G* | Em |

Verse 2

    (Em)   **C**   **D7sus4**
I used to roll the dice,

       G   **Em**
Feel the fear in my enemy's eyes.

         C   **D7sus4**
Listened as the crowd would sing:

       G   **Em**
"Now the old king is dead, long live the king."

        C   **D7sus4**
One minute I held the key,

      G   **Em**
Next the walls were closed on   me.

            C   **D7sus4**
And I discovered that my castles stand,

     G   **Em**
Upon pillars of salt and pil - lars of sand.

Chorus 1

  C   **D7**
I hear Jerusalem bells a-ringing,

G   **Em(add9)**
Roman cavalry choirs are singing.

C   **D7**
Be my mirror my sword and shield,

   G   **Em(add9)**
My missionaries in a foreign field.

C   **D7**
For some reason I can't explain,

G/B   **Em(add9)**
Once you'd gone there was never,

      C **D7**
Never an ho - nest word,

      Gmaj7   **Em***
And that was when I ruled the world.

Interlude 2 | **C6** | **D7*** | **G*** | **Em7** |

                   | **C6** | **D7*** | **G*** | **Em7**   ‖

Verse 3

(Em⁷)   **C**   **D⁷sus⁴**
It was the wicked and wild wind,

          G   **Em**
Blew down the doors to let me in.

                    C   **D⁷sus⁴**
Shattered windows and the sound of drums,

     G   **Em**
People couldn't believe what I'd become.

        C   **D⁷sus⁴**
Revolution - aries wait,

    G   **Em**
For my head on a silver plate.

             C   **D⁷sus⁴**
Just a puppet on a lonely string,

   G   **Em**
Oh, who would ever want to be king?

Chorus 2

  C   **D⁷**
I hear Jerusalem bells a-ringing,

G   **Em(add⁹)**
Roman cavalry choirs are singing.

C   **D⁷**
Be my mirror my sword and shield,

  G   **Em(add⁹)**
My missionaries in a foreign field.

C   **D⁷**
For some reason I can't explain,

 G/B   **Em(add⁹)**
I know St. Peter won't call my name.

    C   **D⁷**
Never an honest word,

     Gmaj⁷   **Em**
But that was when I ruled the world.

Interlude 3　　|| C* | Em* | C* | Em* | |

|| C* | Em* | D7* ||

(D7*)　　　　　　　C　D
Oh, oh, oh, oh, oh,　　oh.

　　　　　　　　　　　G　Em(add9)
Oh, oh, oh, oh, oh,　　oh.

　　　　　　　　　　　C　D7
Oh, oh, oh, oh, oh,　　oh.

　　　　　　　　　　　G　Em(add9)
Oh, oh, oh, oh, oh,　　oh.

Oh, oh, oh, oh, oh.

Chorus 3

C　　　　　　　　D7
Hear Jerusalem bells a-ringing,

G　　　　　　　　Em(add9)
Roman cavalry choirs are singing.

C　　　　　　　　D7
Be my mirror my sword and shield,

　　G　　　　　　　　Em(add9)
My missionaries in a foreign field.

C　　　　　　　　D7
For some reason I can't explain,

　G/B　　　　　　　　Em(add9)
I know St. Peter won't call my name.

　　　　　　Cmaj7　D*
Never an honest word,

　　　　　　　G**　　　　　　Em**
But that was when I ruled the world.

Outro　　| C** | D | Gmaj7 | Em7 | |

| C** | D | Gmaj7 | Em7 || *Repeat to fade*

Walking On A Dream

Words & Music by
Jonathan Sloan, Nicholas Littlemore & Luke Steele

| C | Em7 | D | Am7 | A7sus4 | D/A |

Capo first fret

Intro　　　‖: C　Em7 | Em7　D | C　Em7 | Em7　D :‖

　　　　　Am7　　　　　**A7sus4　D/A　Am7**　　　**A7sus4**　　　**D/A**
　　　　　Walking on a dream,　　　how can I explain?
　　　　　Am7　　　　　**A7sus4　D/A　Am7**　　　**A7sus4**　　　**D/A**
　　　　　Talking to myself,　　　will I see again?

　　　　　　　　　　C　　　　　**Em7**　　　　　　　　　**D**
Pre-chorus 1　We are al - ways running for the thrill of it, thrill of it,
　　　　　　　　　　C　　　　　**Em7**　　　　　　　　　　　　**D**
　　　　　Always push - ing up the hill, searching for the thrill of it.
　　　　　　　　　　C　　　　　**Em7**　　　　　　　　　　　**D**
　　　　　On and on and on we are calling out and out again,
　　　　　　　　　　C　　　　　**Em7**　　　　　　　　　　　　　**D**
　　　　　Never look - ing down, I'm just in awe of what's in front of me.

　　　　　　　　　　C　Em7　　D
Chorus 1　　　Is it real now,
　　　　　　　　　　C　Em7　　　　　　　　　**D**
　　　　　When two people become one?
　　　　　　　　　　C　Em7　　D
　　　　　I can feel it,
　　　　　　　　　　C　Em7　　　　　　　　　　**D**
　　　　　When two people become one.

Link 1　　　‖: C　Em7 | Em7　D | C　Em7 | Em7　D :‖

Verse 1

```
         C                Em7   D
Thought I'd nev - er see,
         C                Em7   D
The love you found in me.
              C           Em7      D
Now it's changing all the time,
         C        Em7                          D
Living in a rhythm where the minutes working overtime.
```

Pre-chorus 2   As Pre-chorus 1

Chorus 2   As Chorus 1

Chorus 3   As Chorus 1

Bridge

```
C   Em7                D      C      Em7  D
      Catch me I'm falling down.
C   Em7                D      C      Em7  D
      Catch me I'm falling down.
```

Verse 2

```
C         Em7      D
    Don't stop just keep going on,
C     Em7                D
I'm     your shoulder, lean upon.
C           Em7        D
    So come on deliver from inside,
C           Em7                  D
All we got is tonight that is right till first light.
```

Chorus 4   As Chorus 1

Chorus 5   As Chorus 1   *To fade*

We Are The People

Words & Music by
Jonathan Sloan, Nicholas Littlemore & Luke Steele

Em   Bm(add11)/D   Cmaj7   Bm(add11)   Am   D11   Dmaj7

Intro | Em | Em | Bm(add11)/D | Bm(add11)/D |

| Cmaj7 | Cmaj7 | Em | Bm(add11)/D ‖

Verse 1

Em   Bm(add11)/D
We can remember   swimming in December,
Cmaj7   Em   Bm(add11)/D
   Heading for the city lights   in nineteen seventy-five.
Em   Bm(add11)/D
   We shared each other   and nearer than farther,
Cmaj7   Em   Bm(add11)/D
   The scent of a lemon drips from your eyes.

Verse 2

Em
   We are the people that rule the world,
Bm(add11)/D
   A force running in every boy and girl.
Cmaj7   Am
   All rejoicing in the world, take me now,
Bm(add11)/D
   We can try.

Verse 3

   Em   **Bm(add¹¹)/D**
  We lived an adventure,   love in the summer.

Cmaj⁷
  Followed the sun till night,

Am   **Bm(add¹¹)/D**   **Em**
Reminiscing other times of life.

                   Bm(add¹¹)/D
For each every other,   the feeling was stronger,

Cmaj⁷   **Am**   **Bm(add¹¹)/D**
  The shock hit eleven, we got lost in your eyes.

Chorus 1

  Cmaj⁷   **Em**
I can't do well when I think you're gonna leave me,

    D¹¹
But I know I try.

       Cmaj⁷   **Em**
Are you gonna leave me now?

         Dmaj⁷
Can't you be be - lieving now?

  Cmaj⁷   **Em**
I can't do well when I think you're gonna leave me,

    D¹¹
But I know I try.

       Cmaj⁷   **Em**
Are you gonna leave me now?

         Dmaj⁷
Can't you be be - lieving now?

Verse 4

 Em
  Can you remember the human life,

Bm(add¹¹)/D   **Cmaj⁷**
  It was still where we'd energize.

                       Am   **Bm(add¹¹)/D** **Em**
Lie in the sand and visualize like it's seventy-five a - gain.

Em
  We are the people that rule the world,

Bm(add¹¹)/D
  A force running in every boy and girl.

Cmaj⁷   **Am**
  All rejoicing in the world, take me now.

Bm(add¹¹)/D
  We can try.

Chorus 2   As Chorus 1

Bridge

Em   **Bm(add11)**
I know everything about you,

                              Cmaj7
Know everything about me,

                              Am   **Bm(add11)**
Know everything about us.

Em   **Bm(add11)**
I know everything about you,

                              Cmaj7
Know everything about me,

                              Am   **Bm(add11)**
Know everything about us.

Chorus 3

‖: **Cmaj7**   **Em**
I can't do well when I think you're gonna leave me,

    D11
But I know I try.

                    Cmaj7   **Em**
Are you gonna leave me now?

                    Dmaj7
Can't you be be - lieving now? :‖ *Repeat 4 times to fade*

Empire Of The Sun

White Winter Hymnal

Words & Music by
Robin Pecknold

E	F#m	A	B7

N.C.(E)

Intro I was following the, I was following the,

I was following the, I was following the,

I was following the, I was following the,

I was following the, I was following the,

E

Verse 1 I was following the pack, all swallowed in their coats,

                      F#m

With scarves of red tied 'round their throats,

To keep their little heads from falling in the snow.

                  A

And I turned 'round and there you go,

                 B7

And, Michael, you would fall and turn the white snow red,

        (E)

As strawberries in the summertime.

Link 1 | E | E | E | E | |

| A | A | E | E | ||

Verse 2   As Verse 1

Instr.

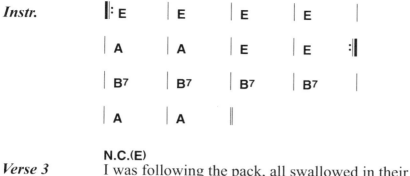

Verse 3

N.C.(E)
I was following the pack, all swallowed in their coats,

(F♯m)
With scarves of red tied 'round their throats,

To keep their little heads from falling in the snow.

(A)
And I turned 'round and there you go,

(B7)
And, Michael, you would fall and turn the white snow red,

(E)
As strawberries in the summertime.

Wire To Wire

Words & Music by
Johnny Borrell

Dm   **C**   **G**

Intro | Dm | Dm | Dm | Dm ||

Verse 1

Dm   C   G
What is love but a strangest of feelings?
Dm   C   G
A sin you swallow for the rest of your life?
Dm   C   G
You've been looking for some - one to be - lieve in,
Dm   C   G   Dm
To love you un - til your eyes run dry.

Verse 2

Dm   C   G
She lives on disil - lusion row,
Dm   C   G
We go where the wild blood flows.
Dm   C   G
On our bodies we share the same scar,
Dm   C   G   Dm
Love me wherev - er you are.

Verse 3

Dm   C   G
How do you love with a faith full of rust?
Dm   C   G
How do you turn what was savage tame?
Dm   C   G
You've been looking for some - one you can trust,
Dm   C   G   Dm
To love you a - gain and a - gain.

Verse 4

Dm   C   G
How do you love in a house without feelings?

Dm   C   G
How do you turn what was savage tame?

Dm   C   G
I've been looking for some - one to be - lieve in,

Dm   C   G   Dm
Love me a - gain and a - gain.

Verse 5

Dm   C   G
She lives by disil - lusion's glow,

Dm   C   G
We go where the wild blood flows.

Dm   C   G   Dm C G
On our bodies, we share the same scar.

Verse 6

Dm   C   G
How do you love on a night without feelings?

Dm   C   G
She says, "Love, I hear sound, I see fury."

Dm   C   G
She says, "Love's not a hostile con - dition."

Dm   C   G   Dm
Love me wherev - er you are.

       C   G   Dm
Love me wherev - er you are.

       C   G   Dm
Love me wherev - er you are,

Wherever you are.

The World We Live In

Words by Brandon Flowers
Music by Brandon Flowers, Dave Keuning, Mark Stoermer & Ronnie Vannucci

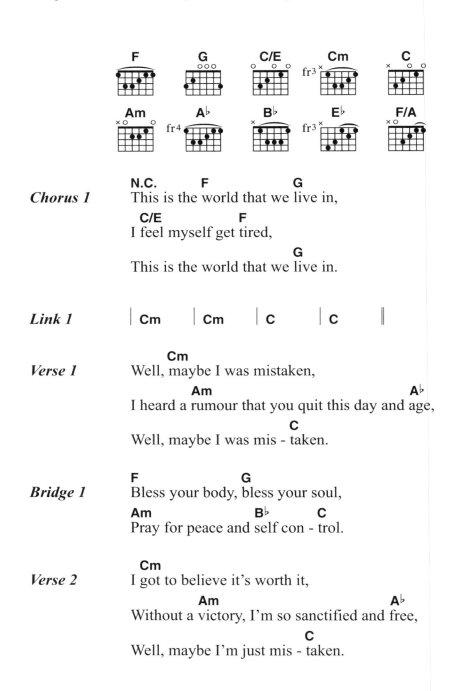

Chorus 1

N.C.　　　F　　　　　　　G
This is the world that we live in,

C/E　　　　　　　F
I feel myself get tired,

　　　　　　　　　　　　　G
This is the world that we live in.

Link 1

| Cm | Cm | C | C ‖

Verse 1

Cm
Well, maybe I was mistaken,

　　　　　Am　　　　　　　　　　　　　　　　Ab
I heard a rumour that you quit this day and age,

　　　　　　　　　　　　　　C
Well, maybe I was mis - taken.

Bridge 1

F　　　　　　　G
Bless your body, bless your soul,

Am　　　　　　　Bb　　　C
Pray for peace and self con - trol.

Verse 2

Cm
I got to believe it's worth it,

　　　　　Am　　　　　　　　　　　　　　　Ab
Without a victory, I'm so sanctified and free,

　　　　　　　　　　　　C
Well, maybe I'm just mis - taken.

Bridge 2

   C/E B♭ C   C/E B♭ C
The lesson learned and the wheels keep turning.

Chorus 2

   C/E   F   G
  This is the world that we live in,

   C/E   F
I can't take blame for two.

                        G
This is the world that we live in,

     C/E   F   G Cm
And maybe we'll make it through, oh.___

Instr.

| Cm | Cm | Am | Am |
| A♭ | A♭ | C | C |

Bridge 3

F   G
Bless your body, bless your soul,

Am   B♭   C
Reel me in and cut my throat.

F   G
Underneath the waterfall,

Am   B♭   C   C/E
Baby we're still in this,   oh yeah.

Chorus 3

C/E   F   G
This is the world that we live in,

   C/E   F
I feel myself get tired,

                        G
This is the world that we live in.

Middle

E♭   Cm   B♭   F/A   A♭
  I had a dream that I was falling   down,

C   C/E
  There's no next time a - round.

  B♭   C
A storm wastes its water on me,

       C/E B♭   C
But my life   was free.

Chorus 4

  C/E   F   G
    I guess it's the world that we live in,

     C/E   F
It's not too late for that.

                         G
This is the world that we live in,

     C/E   F
And no, we can't go back.

                         G
This is the world that we live in,

   C/E   F
I still want something real.

                         G
This is the world that we live in,

        C/E   F   G
I know that we can heal over time.____

C/E   G C/E F
   This is the world that we live in.

G C/E   F
      This is the world that we live in.

Outro 𝄆 F | G | C/E | F 𝄇 *Repeat to fade*

188

Zero

Words & Music by
Nicholas Zinner, Brian Chase & Karen Orzolek

B   A   F#   E   G#m

Intro | B | B | B | B ‖

Verse 1
B   A   F#
Shake it like a ladder to the sun,
B   A   F#
   Makes me feel like a madman on the run.
            E   F#   G#m
Find me never,   never   far gone,
F#   E   F#   B
  So get your   leather, leather,   leather on, on, on, on.

Chorus 1
B
You're zero, what's your name?
A
No one's gonna ask you,
     F#   B
Better find out where they want you to go.

Try and hit the spot,
A
Get to know it in the dark,
F#
Get to know whether you're,
E   F#   G#m
  Crying, crying,   crying, oh, oh.
F#   E   F#   B
Can you   climb, climb,   climb high - er?

Link 1 ‖: B | B | B | B :‖

Verse 2

B   A   F♯
Shake it like a ladder to the sun,
B   A   F♯
   Makes me feel like a madman on the run.
                 E   F♯   G♯m
No you're never,   never   far gone,
F♯   E   F♯   B
   So get your   leather, leather,   leather on, on, on, on.

Chorus 2   As Chorus 1

Link 2   ‖: B | B | B | B :‖

Bridge

B
Was it the cure? Shellshock!

Was it the cure? Hope not!

Was it the cure? Shellshock!

Was it the cure?

What's your name?

Chorus 3   As Chorus 1

Link 3   ‖: B | B | B | B :‖

Outro

B
Was it the cure? Shellshock!

Was it the cure? Hope not!

Was it the cure? Shellshock!

Was it the cure? Hope not!

What's your name?

What's your name?

What's your name?

What's your name?

What's your name?

What's your name?

What's your name?

Oh, oh, oh, oh, oh, oh, oh.

Oh, oh, oh, oh, oh, oh, oh.

Oh, oh, oh, oh, oh, oh, oh.

Oh, oh, oh, oh, oh, oh, oh.

Oh, oh, oh, oh, oh, oh, oh.

Oh, oh, oh, oh, oh, oh, oh.

Yeah Yeah Yeahs